KINDERGARTEN

California Treasures

Practice Book

Macmillan/McGraw-Hill

Contents

The Alphabet

| Aa  | Bb  | Cc  | Dd  | Ee  | Ff  |

| Gg  | Hh  | Ii  | Jj  | Kk  | Ll  |

| Mm  | Nn  | Oo  | Pp  | Qq  | Rr  |

| Ss  | Tt  | Uu  | Vv  | Ww 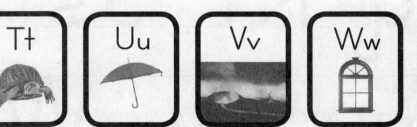 | Xx  |

| Yy  | Zz  |

Name _____

Respond to the Big Book: *Animals in the Park: An ABC Book*
Name the animals. Then draw another animal from the story.

 R 2.4 Retell familiar stories.

Name _____

I

•

I

•

I
•

I

•

High-Frequency Word: *I*
Read the sentences: *I draw. I read. I run. I eat.*

 R 1.15 Read high-frequency words.

©Macmillan/McGraw-Hill

4 Start Smart: We Are Special • Week 1

Aa Bb Cc Dd Ee Ff Gg Hh Ii Jj Kk Ll Mm
Nn Oo Pp Qq Rr Ss Tt Uu Vv Ww Xx Yy Zz

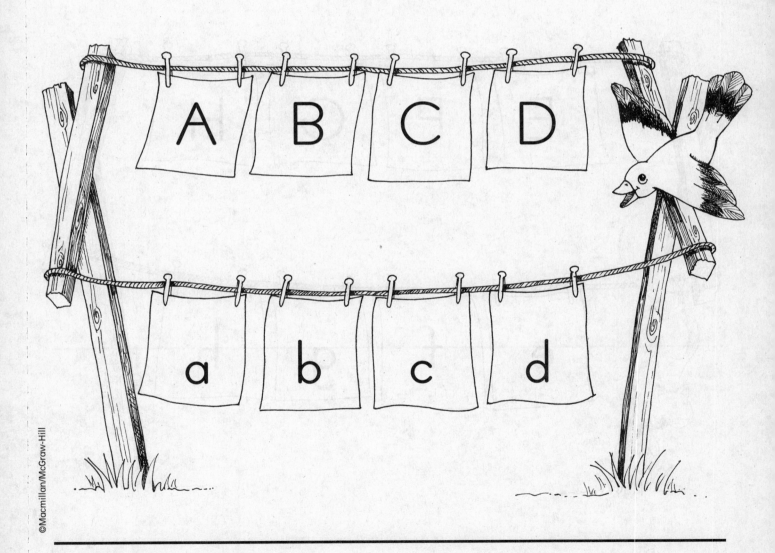

Letter Recognition: *Aa - Dd*
Name each letter. Draw a line to connect the capital and
lowercase forms of the same letter.

R 1.6 Identify uppercase and
lowercase letters.

Name _____

Aa Bb Cc Dd Ee Ff Gg Hh Ii Jj Kk Ll Mm
Nn Oo Pp Qq Rr Ss Tt Uu Vv Ww Xx Yy Zz

©Macmillan/McGraw-Hill

Letter Recognition: Ee - Hh
Name each letter. Draw a line to connect the capital and
lowercase forms of the same letter.

R 1.6 Identify uppercase and
lowercase letters.

Name

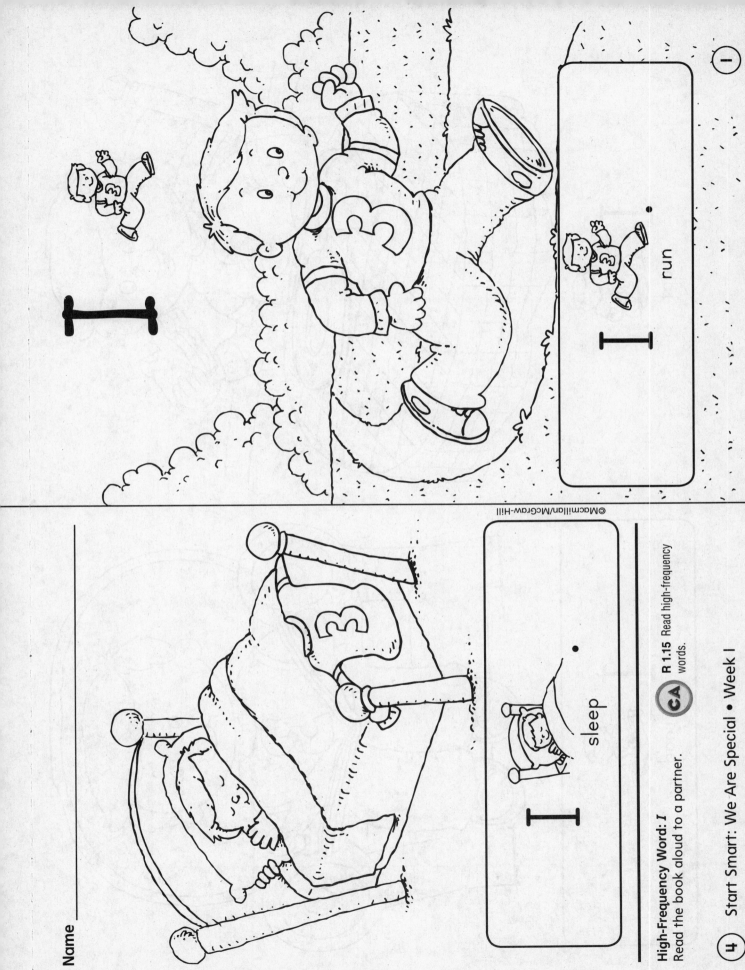

I

I
sleep

I
run

©Macmillan/McGraw-Hill

High-Frequency Word: *I*
Read the book aloud to a partner.

CA **R 1.15** Read high-frequency words.

4 Start Smart: We Are Special • Week I

1

I ___ .

eat

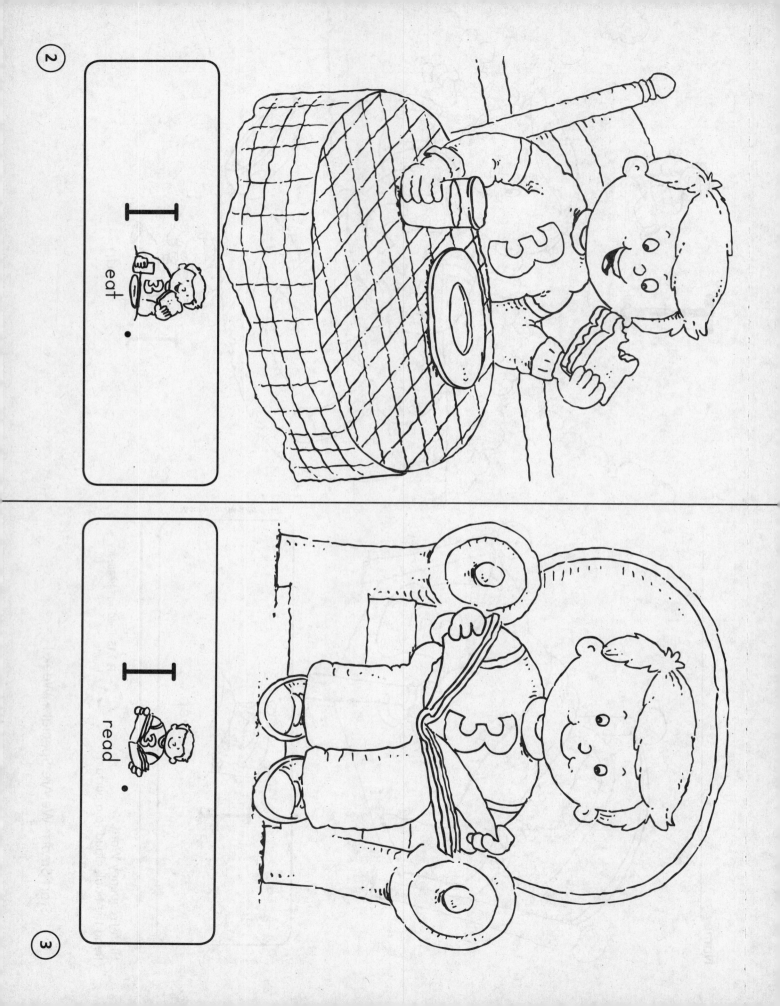

I ___ .

read

Respond to the Big Book: *Hands Can*
Talk about what the children are doing in the pictures.
Trace your hand and tell a partner what your hands can do.

 R 2.4 Retell familiar stories.

Name _____

I can   .

I can   .

I can   .

I can   .

High-Frequency Word: *can*
Read the sentences: *I can clap. I can sing. I can jump. I can kick.*   **CA** R 1.15 Read high-frequency words.

©Macmillan/McGraw-Hill

Name _____

Aa Bb Cc Dd Ee Ff Gg Hh Ii Jj Kk Ll Mm
Nn Oo Pp Qq Rr Ss Tt Uu Vv Ww Xx Yy Zz

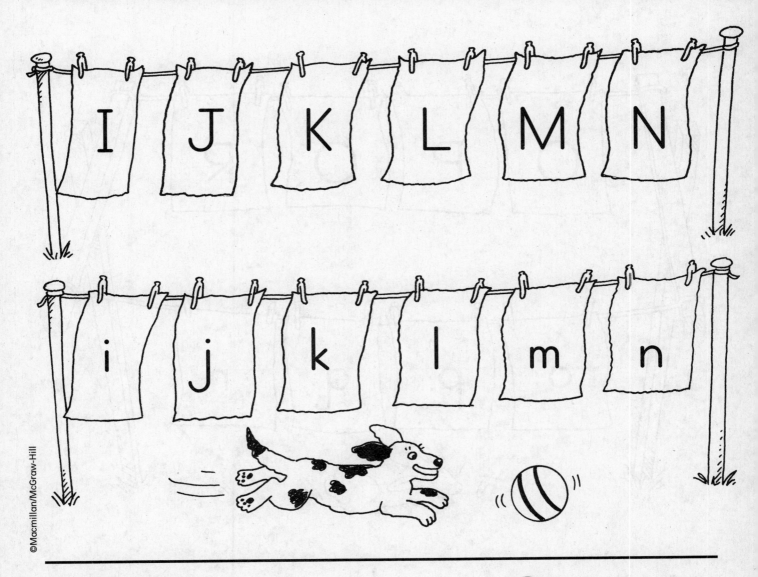

I J K L M N

i j k l m n

Letter Recognition: _Ii - Nn_
Name each letter. Draw a line to connect the capital and
lowercase forms of the same letter.

R 1.6 Identify uppercase and
lowercase letters.

Name _____

Aa Bb Cc Dd Ee Ff Gg Hh Ii Jj Kk Ll Mm
Nn Oo Pp Qq Rr Ss Tt Uu Vv Ww Xx Yy Zz

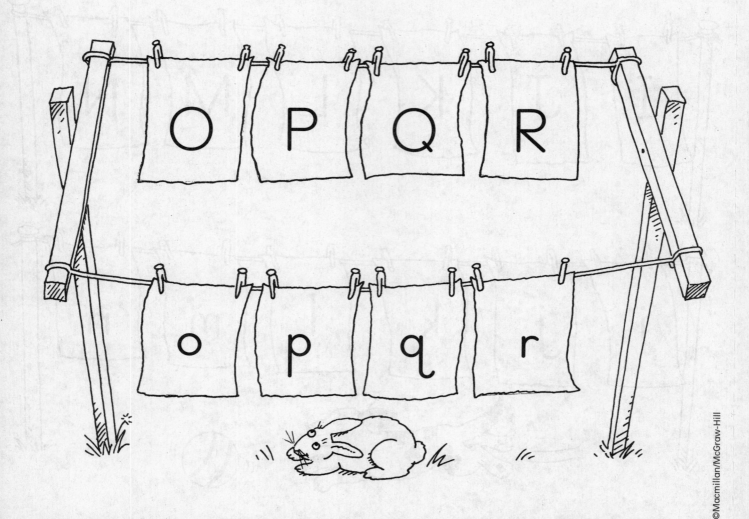

O P Q R

o p q r

©Macmillan/McGraw-Hill

Letter Recognition: *Oo - Rr*
Name each letter. Draw a line to connect the capital and
lowercase forms of the same letter.

CA **R 1.6** Identify uppercase and
lowercase letters.

Name _____

I Can

I can sleep.

I can wash.

High-Frequency Word: *can*
Read the book aloud to a partner.

R 1.15 Read high-frequency words.

Start Smart: We Are Special • Week 2

I can

4

1

I can

brush

I can

hug

Respond to the Big Book: *Jazz Baby*
Look at the pictures and name the instruments. Draw a circle
around the two pictures that are the same. Which picture
is different?

 R 2.4 Retell familiar stories.

Start Smart: We Are Special • Week 3   15

Name _____

🍎 I can  .

⭐ I can  .

🌲 I can  .

🐟 I can  .

High-Frequency Words: *I, can*
Read the sentences: *I can sing. I can dance. I can play. I can clap.*

CA **R 1.15** Read high-frequency words.

Aa Bb Cc Dd Ee Ff Gg Hh Ii Jj Kk Ll Mm
Nn Oo Pp Qq Rr Ss Tt Uu Vv Ww Xx Yy Zz

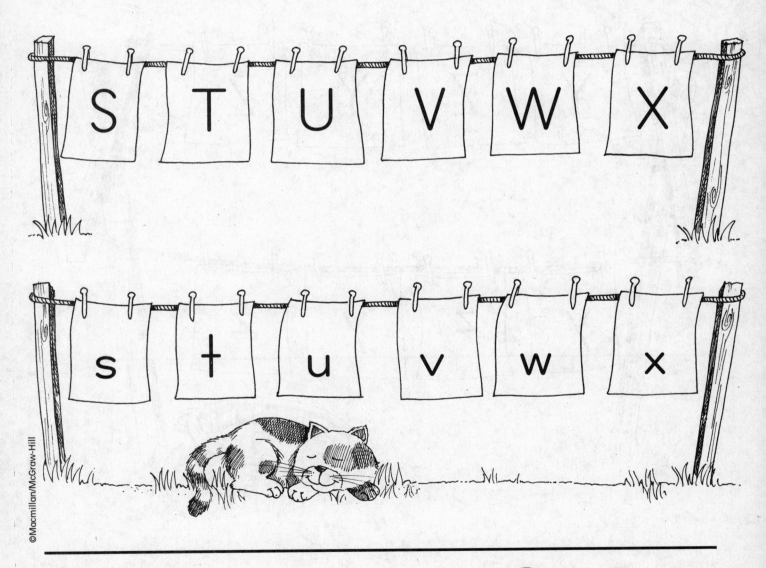

S T U V W X

s t u v w x

Letter Recognition: Ss - Xx
Name each letter. Draw a line to connect the capital and
lowercase forms of the same letter.

 CA **R 1.6** Identify uppercase and
lowercase letters.

Name _____

Aa Bb Cc Dd Ee Ff Gg Hh Ii Jj Kk Ll Mm
Nn Oo Pp Qq Rr Ss Tt Uu Vv Ww Xx Yy Zz

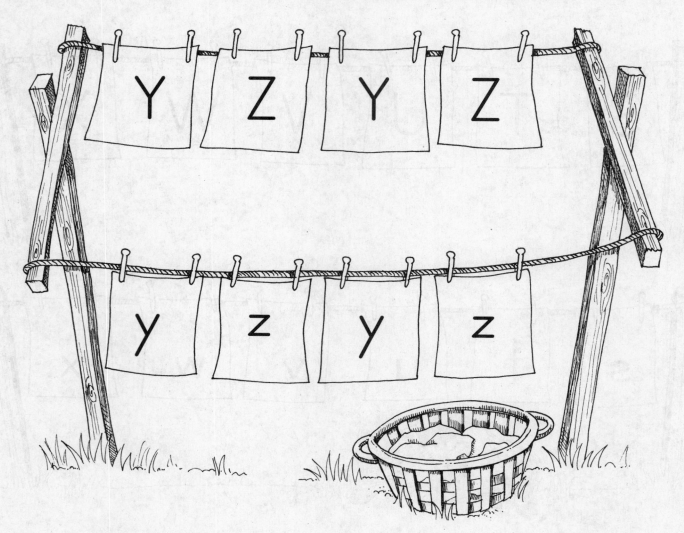

Y Z Y Z

y z y z

Letter Recognition: _Yy - Zz_
Name each letter. Draw a line to connect the capital and
lowercase forms of the same letter.

 R 1.6 Identify uppercase and
lowercase letters.

Name _____

I Can

I can

I can run.

I can

I can clap.

©Macmillan/McGraw-Hill

High-Frequency Words: *I, can*
Read the book aloud to a partner.

CA **R 1.15** Read high-frequency words.

Start Smart: We Are Special • Week 3

1

4

I can _____.

kick

2

I can _____.

jump

3

Name _____

WELCOME

m

Phonics: /m/*m*
Look at the picture. Say the name of each item. Circle each
item whose name begins with the same sound as *monkey*.
Write the letter.

CA **R 1.14** Match sounds to letters.

Name _____

©Macmillan/McGraw-Hill

Comprehension: Make Predictions *Whose Baby Am I?*
Look at the baby animals. Name each animal.
Draw a line from the baby animal to the adult animal you
think it will grow into.

CA **R 2.2** Make predictions.

We Can

We can

paint .

Name _____

ABCDEFGHIJKLM
NOPQRSTUVWXYZ
abcdefghijk
lmnopqrst
uvwxyz

We can

hug .

High-Frequency Word: *we*
Read the book aloud to a
partner. Reread for fluency.

R 1.15 Read high-frequency
words.

CA

We can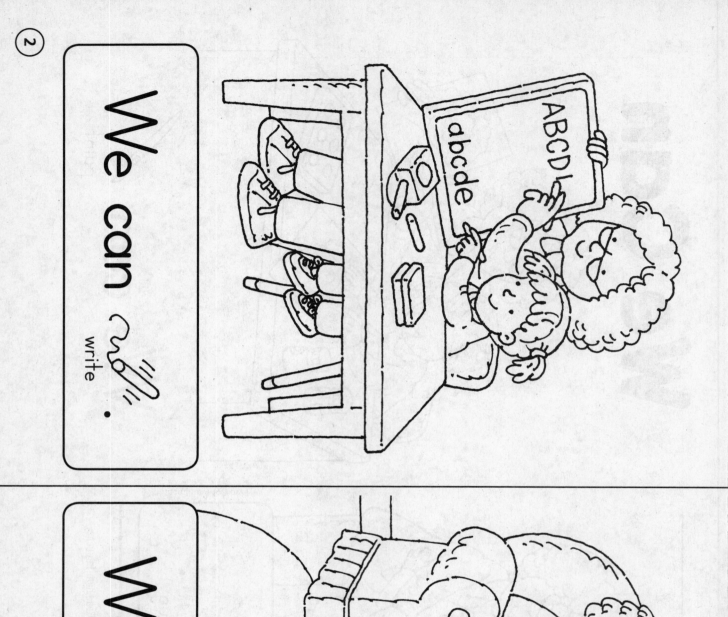
write.

We can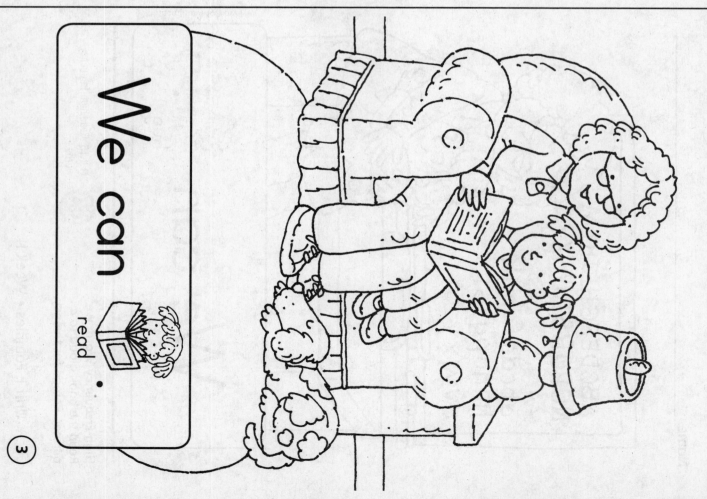
read.

Name _____

Phonemic Awareness: /m/
Look at the pictures. Say the name of each item. Circle the item if its name begins with the same sound you hear at the beginning of *monkey*.

R 1.11 Distinguish words by beginning sounds.

Name _____

Mm

_____   _____   _____

m _ _ _ _ _   _ _ _ _ _ _ _ _ _   _ _ _ _ _ _ _ _ _

_____   _____   _____

_____   _____   _____

_ _ _ _ _ _ _ _ _   _ _ _ _ _ _ _ _ _   _ _ _ _ _ _ _ _ _

_____   _____   _____

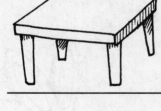

_____   _____   _____

_ _ _ _ _ _ _ _ _   _ _ _ _ _ _ _ _ _   _ _ _ _ _ _ _ _ _

_____   _____   _____

Phonics: /m/m
Say the name of each picture. Write the letter below
each picture whose name begins with the /m/ sound.

 R 1.14 Match sounds to letters.

Aa

Name _____

_____ _____ _____ _____

a ------ ------- -------- --------

_____ _____ _____ _____

©Macmillan/McGraw-Hill

Phonics: /a/a
Look at the picture. Say the name of each item. Circle each item
whose name begins with the same sound as *apple*. Write the letter.

 R 1.14 Match sounds to letters.

Name _____

Literary Analysis: Setting

 Circle the picture that shows a family working in a garden.

★ Circle the picture that shows a family at the store.

 R 3.3 Identify settings.

©Macmillan/McGraw-Hill

28 Unit I: Families • Week 2

Name

the

the dog

High-Frequency Word: *the*
Read the book aloud to a partner.
Reread for fluency.

CA **R 1.15** Read high-frequency words.

4 Unit I: Families • Week 2

©Macmillan/McGraw-Hill

The

the boy

1

the

girl

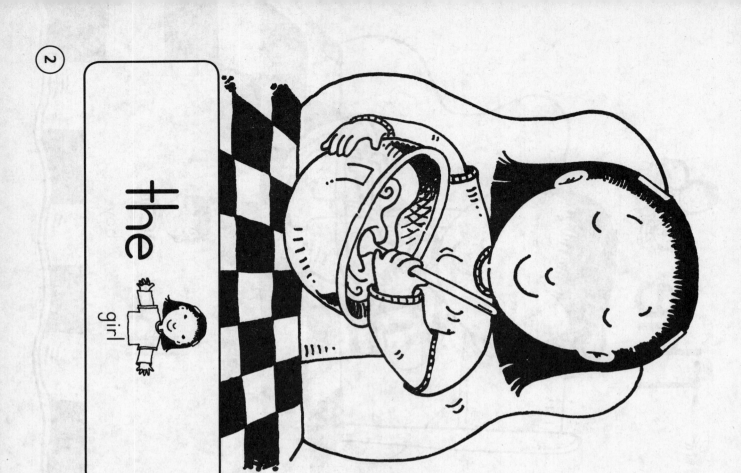

the

mom

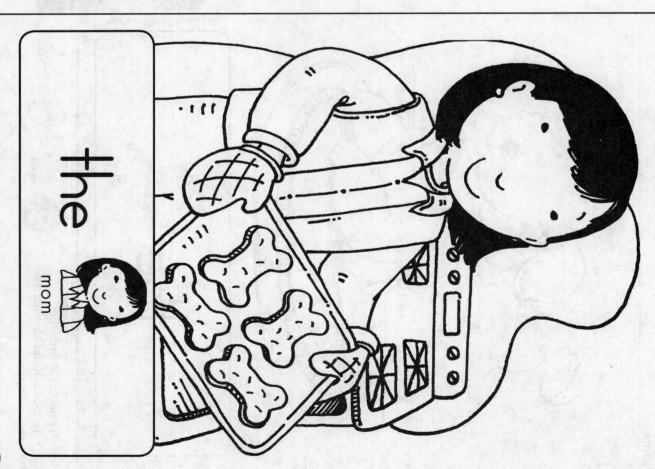

Name _____

Phonemic Awareness: /a/
Look at the picture. Say the name of each item. Circle the
item if its name begins with the same sound you hear at the
beginning of *astronaut*.

 R 1.11 Distinguish words by
beginning sounds.

Unit I: Families • Week 2   31

Write

Name _____

am →

I am  .
happy

I _____  .
sad

I _____ .
mad

Phonics: Blending *am*
Blend the sounds and say the word.
Read the sentence. Write the word. Read the sentence again.

 R 1.15 Read one-syllable words.

©Macmillan/McGraw-Hill

 **Mm**

Name _____

_____ m _____

_____ _____ _____

_____ _____ _____

_____ _____ _____

 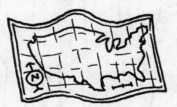 

_____ _____ _____

_____ _____ _____

Phonics: /m/m
Say the name of each picture. Write the letter below each picture whose name begins with the /m/ sound.

 CA **R 1.14** Match sounds to letters.

Name _____

©Macmillan/McGraw-Hill

Comprehension: Make Predictions
Look at the big picture. Tell what is happening. Circle the picture
that shows what might happen next.

CA   **R 2.2** Make predictions.

34   Unit I: Families • Week 3

I Can

I can run.

@Macmillan/McGraw-Hill

Name _____

We can eat.

High-Frequency Words: *we, the*
Read the book aloud to a
partner. Reread for fluency.

CA **R 1.15** Read high-frequency
words.

④ Unit I: Families • Week 3

We can
run
.

The
dog
can
run
.

 **Aa**

Name _____

 Write

_____   _____   _____

- - - - - - - - -   - - - - - - - - -   - - - - - - - - -

_____   _____   _____

★

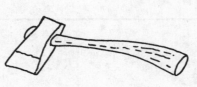 

_____   _____   _____

- - - - - - - - -   - - - - - - - - -   - - - - - - - - -

_____   _____   _____

🌲

_____   _____   _____

- - - - - - - - -   - - - - - - - - -   - - - - - - - - -

_____   _____   _____

©Macmillan/McGraw-Hill

Phonics: /a/a
Say the name of each picture. Write the letter below each
picture whose name begins with the /a/ sound.

(CA) **R 1.14** Match sounds to letters.

Write

Name _____

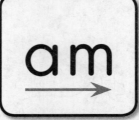
am →

I ___ am .
mad

I ___ .
sad

I ___ .
happy

Phonics: Blending _am_
Blend the sounds and say the word. Read the sentence.
Write the word _am_. Read the sentence again.

 R 1.15 Read one-syllable words.

©Macmillan/McGraw-Hill

Phonics: /m/m and /a/a
Cut out the pictures. Say the name of each picture. Glue it below
the monkey if it begins with the /m/ sound. Glue it below the
alligator if it begins with the /a/ sound.

CA **R 1.14** Match sounds to letters.

Name _____

Name

Name

Name

Phonics: /m/m and /a/a
Say the name of each animal and its beginning sound and letter.
Write your name. Cut out the bookmarks. Use them to hold your
place when reading a book.

Ss

Name _____

S

Phonics: /s/s

Look at the picture. Say the name of each item. Circle each item whose name begins with the same sound as *sun*. Write the letter.

 R 1.14 Match sounds to letters.

Name _____

Literary Analysis: Character

🍎 Circle the picture that shows two characters working together.

⭐ Circle the picture that shows a character painting.

🌲 Circle the picture that shows two characters reading together.

 R 3.3 Identify characters.

42 Unit 2: Friends • Week I

We Like Sam!

We like

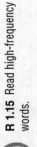

apples.

1

Name

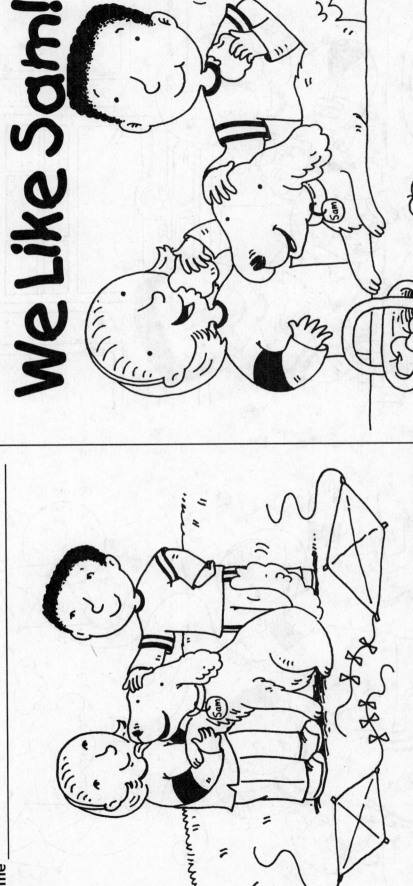

We like

Sam.

©Macmillan/McGraw-Hill

High-Frequency Word: *like*
Read the book aloud to a partner.
Reread for fluency.

CA **R 1.15** Read high-frequency words.

4 Unit 2: Friends • Week 1

We like

sandwiches.

We like

kites.

Name _____

Phonemic Awareness: /s/
Look at the picture. Say the name of each item. Circle the item if its
name begins with the same sound you hear at the beginning of *sun*.

CA **R 1.11** Distinguish words by beginning sounds.

Unit 2: Friends • Week 1 **45**

©Macmillan/McGraw-Hill

Name _____

Sam →

 Am I Sam ?

 I am _____ .

 I like _____ .

Phonics: Blending s
Blend the sounds and say the word. Read the sentence.
Write the word *Sam*. Read the sentence again.

 R 1.15 Read one-syllable words.

©Macmillan/McGraw-Hill

P p

Name _____

Write

p _ _ _ _ _ _ _ _ _ _ _

©Macmillan/McGraw-Hill

Phonics: /p/p

Look at the picture. Say the name of each item. Circle each item whose name begins with the same sound as *pig*. Write the letter.

CA **R 1.14** Match sounds to letters.

Unit 2: Friends • Week 2   **47**

Circle

Name _____

©Macmillan/McGraw-Hill

Comprehension: Compare and Contrast
Look at the picture. Circle all of the food. Draw a line under the fruit. Talk with a partner about how the fruit is the same and different from the other foods.

R 1.18 Describe objects in specific language.

48 Unit 2: Friends • Week 2

Name _____

I Like

I like a 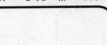.
cherry

I like a .
peach

High-Frequency Word: *a*
Read the book aloud to a partner.
Reread for fluency.

(CA) **R 1.15** Read high-frequency words.

④ Unit 2: Friends • Week 2

①

I like a .

pear

I like a .

banana

Name _____

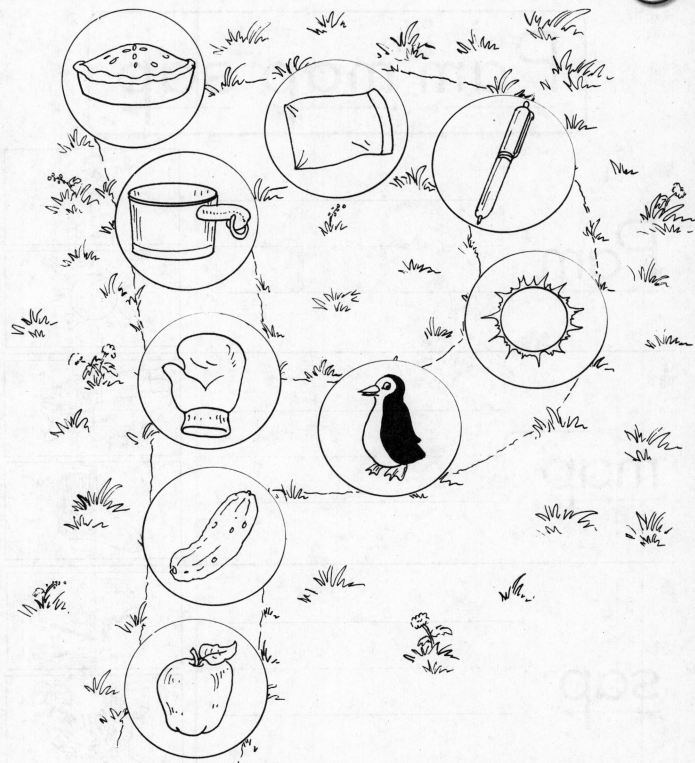

Phonemic Awareness: /p/
Look at the picture. Say the name of each item on the path.
Color the item if its name begins with the same sound you
hear at the beginning of *path*.

 R 1.11 Distinguish words by beginning sounds.

Name _____

Pam map sap

Pam _____

map _____

sap _____

Phonics: Blending with /p/p
Blend the sounds and say the word. Write the word. Then circle the picture that goes with the word.

 R 1.15 Read one-syllable words.

©Macmillan/McGraw-Hill

S s

Name _____

_____ _____ _____ _____

s _____ _____ _____

©Macmillan/McGraw-Hill

Phonics: /s/s
Look at the picture. Say the name of each item. Circle each item whose name begins with the same sound as *sun*. Write the letter.

CA **R 1.14** Match sounds to letters.

Name _____

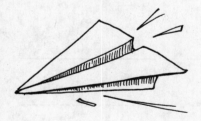  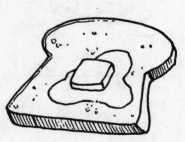

Literary Analysis: Character *Simon and Molly plus Hester*
Name the characters. Then draw a line to match the
characters to what they do with a friend in the story.

 R 3.3 Identify characters.

We Like

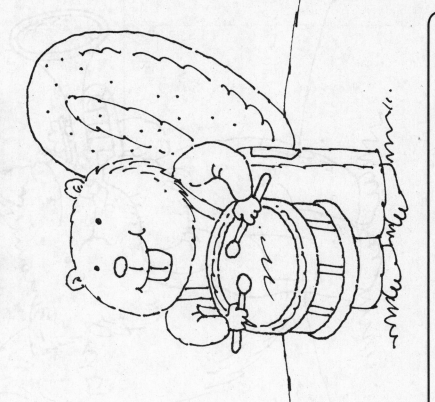

I like a

drum

Name _____

We like

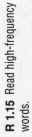

music

High-Frequency Words: *like, a*
Read the book aloud to a
partner. Reread for fluency.

CA **R 1.15** Read high-frequency words.

④ Unit 2: Friends • Week 3

I like a

horn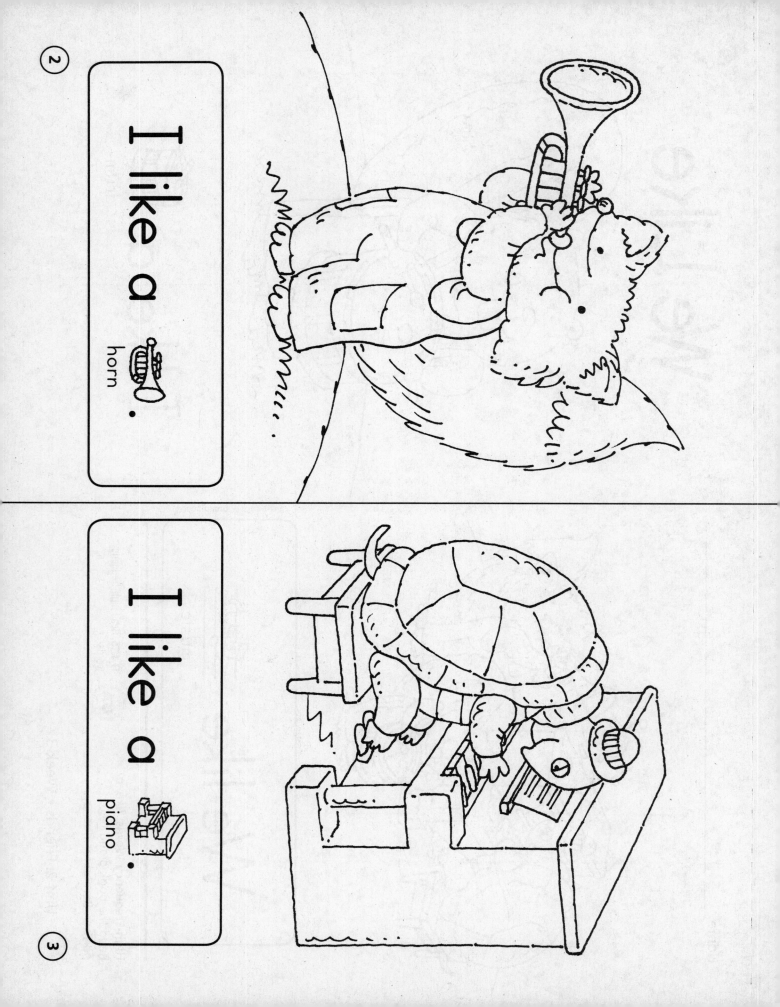

I like a

piano

Pp

Name _____

p

★

🌲

©Macmillan/McGraw-Hill

Phonics: /p/p
Say the name of each picture. Write the letter below
each picture whose name begins with the /p/ sound.

 R 1.14 Match sounds to letters.

Sam Pam map sap

🍎 Sam  ~~Sam~~

⭐ Pam

🌲 map

🐟 sap

Phonics: Blending *s*, *p*
Blend the sounds and say the word. Write the word.
Repeat the word.

 R 1.15 Read one-syllable words.

Phonemic Awareness: /s/, /p/
Say the name of each picture. Put a marker on each picture if its
name begins with the /p/ sound.
Play again. Put a marker on each picture if its name begins with the
/s/ sound.

 R 1.11 Distinguish words by
beginning sounds.

Write

Name _____

©Macmillan/McGraw-Hill

Phonics: /s/s, /p/p
Say the name of each picture. Write the letter that stands for the sound you hear at the beginning of each word.

 R 1.14 Match sounds to letters.

T t

Name _____

_____ | _____ | _____ | _____

Phonics: /t/t
Look at the picture. Say the name of each item. Circle each item
whose name begins with the same sound as *turtle*. Write the letter.

CA R 1.14 Match sounds to letters.

©Macmillan/McGraw-Hill

Name _____

Comprehension: Make Predictions

Look at the top picture. Draw a line to the picture below that shows what might happen next.

CA R 2.2 Make predictions.

©Macmillan/McGraw-Hill

I See Pam!

I see the .

I see the

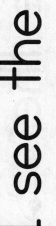
flower

Name _____

I see Pam!

High-Frequency Word: *see*
Read the book aloud to a partner.
Reread for fluency.

CA **R 1.15** Read high-frequency words.

④ Unit 3: Transportation • Week 1

I see the

car
.

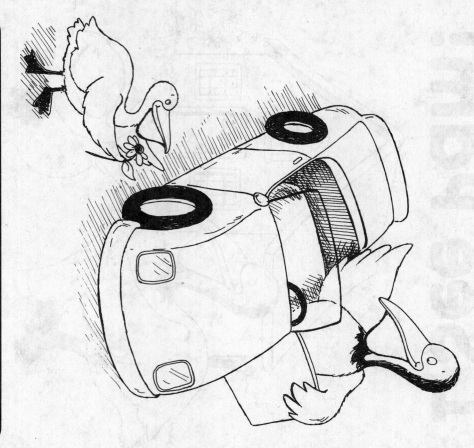

I see the
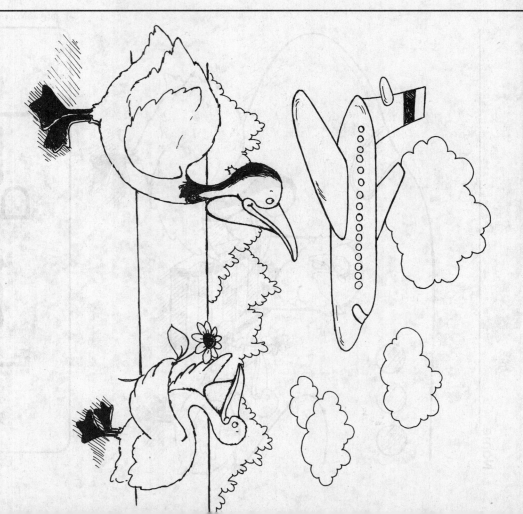
plane
.

Phonemic Awareness: /t/
Look at the pictures. Say the name of each item. Color the
item if its name begins with the same sound you hear at the
beginning of *turtle*.

 R 1.11 Distinguish words by
beginning sounds.

Write

Name _____

at sat

•

I am _at_ the school .

★

I _____ at the table .

🌲

I am _____ the house .

Phonics: Blending _at_
Blend the sounds and say the word. Read the sentence. Write the
word that completes the sentence. Read the sentence again.

CA R 1.15 Read one-syllable words.

©Macmillan/McGraw-Hill

I i

Name _____

i

Phonics: /i/i
Look at the picture. Say the name of each item on the path.
Circle each item whose name begins with the same sound as
iguana. Write the letter.

 R 1.14 Match sounds to letters.

©Macmillan/McGraw-Hill

Name _____

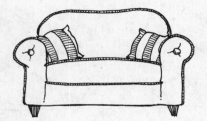  

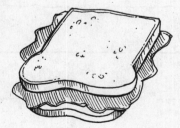 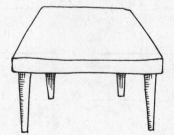 

Vocabulary: Classify and Categorize
Name the pictures in each row. Draw an X on the picture that does not belong. Tell why it does not belong.

 R 1.17 Sort words into categories.

©Macmillan/McGraw-Hill

Can We Go?

Can we go?

©Macmillan/McGraw-Hill

Name _____

The boat can go.

High-Frequency Word: go
Read the book aloud to a partner.
Reread for fluency.

CA **R 1.15** Read high-frequency words.

Unit 3: Transportation • Week 2

We can go!

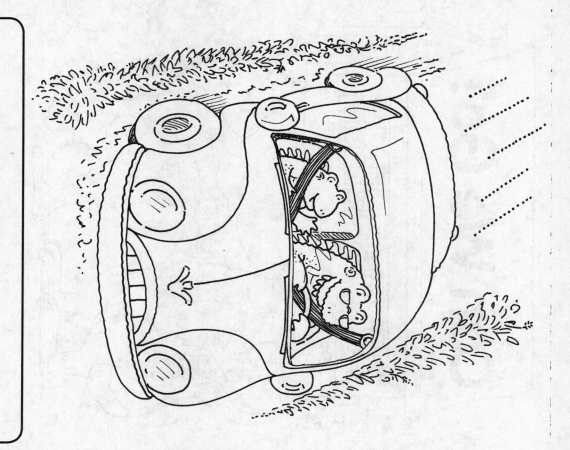

We see the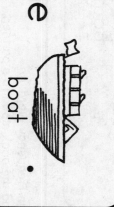
boat
.

Name _____

Phonemic Awareness: /i/
Look at the pictures. Say the name of each item. Circle the item if its name begins with the same sound you hear at the beginning of *inchworm*.

CA **R 1.11** Distinguish words by beginning sounds.

©Macmillan/McGraw-Hill

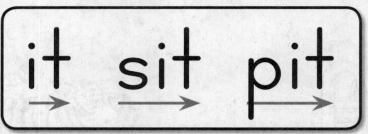

it sit pit

it →

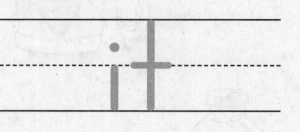

sit →

pit →

Phonics: Blending _it_
Blend the sounds and say the word. Write the word. Repeat the word. **CA** R 1.15 Read one-syllable words.

Tt

Name _____

🍎

_____   _____   _____

- - - - - - +- - - - -   - - - - - - - - - - -   - - - - - - - - - - -

_____   _____   _____

★

_____   _____   _____

- - - - - - - - - -   - - - - - - - - - -   - - - - - - - - - -

_____   _____   _____

🌲

_____   _____   _____

- - - - - - - - - -   - - - - - - - - - -   - - - - - - - - - -

_____   _____   _____

Phonics: /t/*t*
Say the name of each picture. Write the letter below each picture
whose name begins with the /t/ sound.

CA **R 1.14** Match sounds to letters.

Name _____

Literary Analysis: Character, Plot *Duck on a Bike*

 Circle the picture that shows what happened at the beginning of the story.

★ Circle the character who always wanted to ride a bike.

CA R 3.3 Identify characters and events.

©Macmillan/McGraw-Hill

74 Unit 3: Transportation • Week 3

We Can Go!

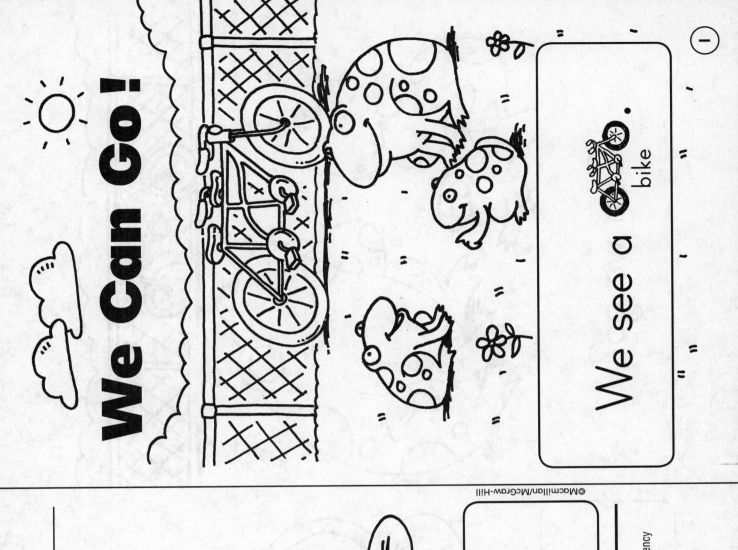

We see a bike.

Name _____

We like the bike.

High-Frequency Words: *see, go*
Read the book aloud to a partner.
Reread for fluency.

CA **R 1.15** Read high-frequency words.

(4) Unit 3: Transportation • Week 3

Can we go?

We can go!

I i

Name _____

🍎

Ink

i

⭐

1

Soop

🌲

Phonics: /i/i
Say the name of each picture. Write the letter below each picture
whose name begins with the /i/ sound.

 R 1.14 Match sounds to letters.

©Macmillan/McGraw-Hill

Name _____

it sit Pat

 We see _____ it _____ .

 It can _____ .

 We like _____ .

Phonics: Blending /i/i, /t/t
Blend the sounds and say each word. Read the sentence. Write the
word that completes the sentence. Read the sentence again.

 R 1.15 Read one-syllable words.

Draw

Ink

Tt

You're
Invited
to a
Party

©Macmillan/McGraw-Hill

Phonics: /t/t
Say the name of each picture. Draw a line from the pictures that
begin with the /t/ sound to the tent.

R 1.14 Match sounds to letters.

Name _____

Phonics: /i/i
Say the name of each picture. Draw a line from the pictures that begin with the /i/ sound to the *iguana*.

CA R 1.14 Match sounds to letters.

©Macmillan/McGraw-Hill

80 Unit 3: Transportation • Week 3

Nn

Name _____

🍎

n

⭐

9

🌲

🐟

Phonics: /n/n
Say the name of each picture. Write the letter next to each picture whose name begins with the /n/ sound.

CA R I.14 Match sounds to letters.

Name _____

_____

- - - - - - - - - - - - - - - -

_____

_____

- - - - - - - - - - - - - - - -

_____

_____

- - - - - - - - - - - - - - - -

_____

Comprehension: Sequence *Apple Farmer Annie*
Look at the pictures. Write 1, 2, and 3 to show what happened first, next, and last.

 R 2.4 Retell familiar stories.

©Macmillan/McGraw-Hill

Nip, Nat

We like to sit.

Name

We like to go.

High-Frequency Word: *to*
Read the book aloud to a partner.
Reread for fluency.

CA **R 1.15** Read high-frequency words.

We like to

nap.

We like to see.

Name _____

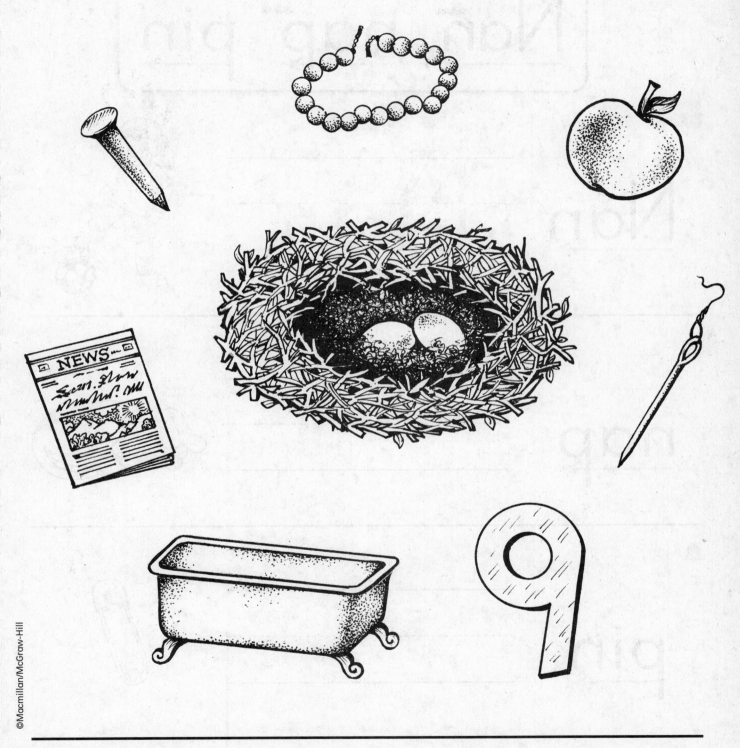

Phonemic Awareness: /n/

Look at the pictures. Say the name of each item. Circle the item if its name begins with the same sound you hear at the beginning of *nest*.

 R 1.11 Distinguish words by beginning sounds.

Write

Name _____

Nan nap pin

Nan — Nan

nap _____

---

pin _____

©Macmillan/McGraw-Hill

Phonics: Blending _n_
Blend the sounds and say the word. Write the word. Repeat the word.

 R 1.15 Read one-syllable words.

C c

Name _____

🍎

_____
C
_____

🌟
- - - - - - - - -

- - - - - - - - -

🌲
- - - - - - - - -

- - - - - - - - -

- - - - - - - - -

- - - - - - - - -

Phonics: /k/c
Say the name of each picture. Write the letter next to each
picture whose name begins with the /k/ sound.

CA **R 1.14** Match sounds to letters.

©Macmillan/McGraw-Hill

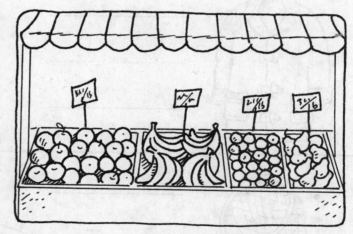

Comprehension: Make Inferences
Look at the pictures. Draw a line from each worker to the place where he or she works. Talk about what each worker does.

 R 2.3 Connect information to life experiences.

©Macmillan/McGraw-Hill

I Have a

cat

I have a  .

cat

1

Name _____

I have to go.

@Macmillan/McGraw-Hill

High-Frequency Word: *have*
Read the book aloud to a partner. Reread for fluency.

CA **R 1.15** Read high-frequency words.

4 Unit 4: Food • Week 2

I have a .

can

I have a .

cap

Phonemic Awareness: /k/c
Look at the picture. Say the name of each item. Circle the item
if its name begins with the same sound that you hear at the
beginning of *cat.*

 R 1.11 Distinguish words by
beginning sounds.

Write

Name _____

Cam cap can cat

🍎 Cam   Cam

⭐ cap

🌲 can

🐟 cat

Phonics: Blending c
Blend the sounds and say the word. Write the word. Repeat the word. **R 1.15** Read one-syllable words.

©Macmillan/McGraw-Hill

Nn

Name _____

🍎

n

⭐

9

🌲 SCHOOL BUS

🐟

Phonics: /n/n
Say the name of each picture. Write the letter next to each picture whose name begins with the /n/ sound.

CA **R 1.14** Match sounds to letters.

©Macmillan/McGraw-Hill

Draw

Name _____

Comprehension: Make Inferences
Look at the top picture. Then look at the pictures below. Draw a line
to the picture below that shows what the characters might do.

CA **R 2.3** Connect information
to life experiences.

©Macmillan/McGraw-Hill

94 Unit 4: Food • Week 3

I Nap

I have to nap.

1

Name _____

I have to sip.

I have

High-Frequency Words: *to, have*
Read the book aloud to a partner.
Reread for fluency.

CA **R 1.15** Read high-frequency words.

4 Unit 4: Food • Week 3

I have to pin.

I have to sit.

Cc

Name _____

©Macmillan/McGraw-Hill

C

Phonics: /k/c
Look at the picture. Say the name of each item. Circle each item
whose name begins with the same sound as *cat*. Write the letter.

 R 1.14 Match sounds to letters.

Unit 4: Food • Week 3   **97**

Nan can nap

I am _Nan_.

I _____ tap.

I can _____.

Phonics: Blending _n, c_
Blend the sounds and say the word. Read the sentence.
Write the word that completes the sentence. Read the sentence again.

 R 1.15 Read one-syllable words.

©Macmillan/McGraw-Hill

Phonics: /n/n, /k/c
Say the name of each item and the letter it begins with. Turn the
picture over and trace the letter.

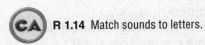 **R 1.14** Match sounds to letters.

c   n   c   c

c   n   n   c

n   c   n   n

Phonics: /n/n, /k/c
Trace the letters. Say each letter and its sound.
Name a word that begins with the letter.

Oo

Name _____

_____

- - - - - - - - - - - -

_____

_____

- - - - - - - - - - - -

_____

★

_____

- - - - - - - - - - - -

_____

_____

- - - - - - - - - - - -

_____

_____

- - - - - - - - - - - -

_____

_____

- - - - - - - - - - - -

_____

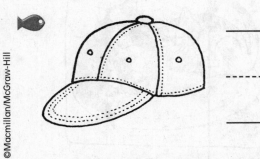

_____

- - - - - - - - - - - -

_____

_____

- - - - - - - - - - - -

_____

Phonics: /o/o
Say the name of each picture. Write the letter next to
each picture whose name begins with the /o/ sound.

CA **R 1.14** Match sounds to letters.

Unit 5: Animals • Week 1   **101**

Name _____

Comprehension: Make Predictions *Mama Cat Has Three Kittens*
Look at the big picture. Then look at the two small pictures. Draw
a line to the picture that shows what might happen next.

 R 2.2 Make predictions.

©Macmillan/McGraw-Hill

It Is!

It is in the .
tree

©Macmillan/McGraw-Hill

①

Name _____

It is in the .
grass

High-Frequency Word: *is*
Read the book aloud to a partner.
Reread for fluency.

(CA) **R 1.15** Read high-frequency words.

④ Unit 5: Animals • Week 1

It is in the 
flowers

It is in the 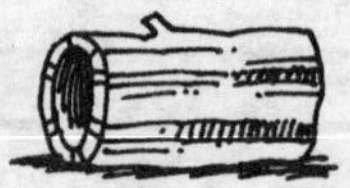
log

Name _____

 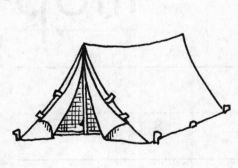  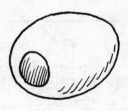

©Macmillan/McGraw-Hill

Phonemic Awareness: /o/
Say the name of each picture. Circle the picture if its name begins
with the same sound you hear at the beginning of *octopus*.

CA **R 1.11** Distinguish words by beginning sounds.

Unit 5: Animals • Week 1   105

Name _____

cot

pot

pot

pop

pan

mom

mat

map

mop

Phonics: Blending /o/o
Blend the sounds and say each word. Then circle the word that
names the picture. Write the word that names the picture.

 R 1.15 Read one-syllable words.

Ff

Name _____

Write

🍎 _____
f
_____

⭐ _____
_____

🌲 _____
_____

🐟 _____

_____

Phonics: /f/ f
Say the name of each picture. Write the letter next to each picture whose name begins with the /f/ sound.

CA R 1.14 Match sounds to letters.

Unit 5: Animals • Week 2   107

©Macmillan/McGraw-Hill

Name _____

  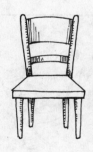

Vocabulary: Classify and Categorize
Say the name of each item. Circle the animals. Draw a line under the things that are not animals.

CA **R 1.17** Sorts words into categories.

Name ___

Play

A ___ can play.
dog

A ___ can play.
pig

©Macmillan/McGraw-Hill

High-Frequency Word: *play*
Read the book aloud to a partner.
Reread for fluency.

 **R 1.15** Read high-frequency words.

4 Unit 5: Animals • Week 2

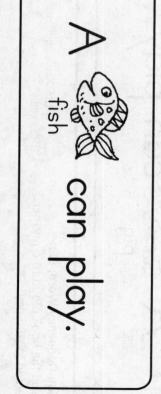

A
cub

can play.

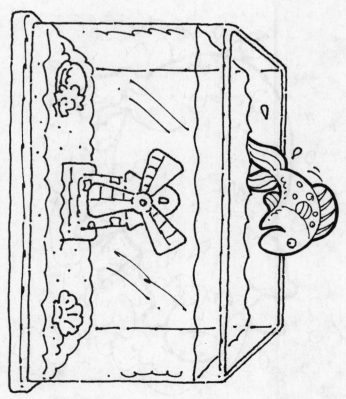

A
fish

can play.

Name _____

©Macmillan/McGraw-Hill

Phonemic Awareness: /f/
Look at the picture. Say the name of each item. Circle the item
if its name begins with the same sound you hear at the beginning
of *fish*.

 R 1.11 Distinguish words by beginning sounds.

Name _____

fan fit fin

I have a ___ **fan** .

Can it ___?

I see a ___.

Phonics: Blending f
Blend the sounds and say each word. Read the sentence. Write the word that completes the sentence. Read the sentence again.

 R 1.15 Read one-syllable words.

©Macmillan/McGraw-Hill

Circle

 Oo

Name _____

_____

- - - - - - - - - - - - - -

_____

★

_____

- - - - - - - - - - - - - -

_____

🌲

_____

- - - - - - - - - - - - - -

_____

©Macmillan/McGraw-Hill

Phonics: /o/o
Say the name of each picture. Circle each picture whose name
begins with the same sound as *octopus.* Write the letter.

CA **R 1.14** Match sounds to letters.

Unit 5: Animals • Week 3   **113**

Name _____

Literary Analysis: Plot, Character *Mole and the Baby Bird*
Draw a line to match the characters to what they did in the story.

 R 3.3 Identify characters and events.

©Macmillan/McGraw-Hill

114 Unit 5: Animals • Week 3

Name _____

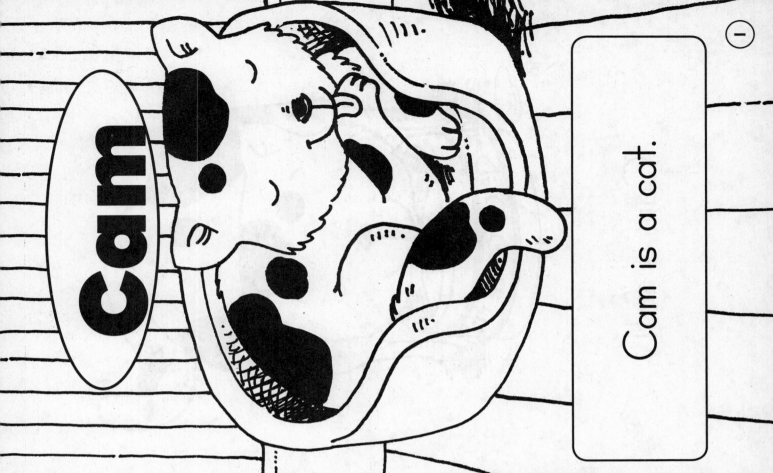

Cam

Cam is a cat.

©Macmillan/McGraw-Hill

Cam can play in a cap.

High-Frequency Words: *is, play*
Read the book aloud to a partner.
Reread for fluency.

 R 1.15 Read high-frequency words.

④ Unit 5: Animals • Week 3

①

Cam is fat!

Cam can play in a  hat .

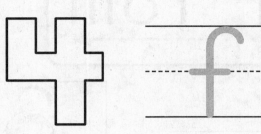

Name _____

4   f   - - - - - - - - -   6   - - - - - - - - -

Phonics: /f/f
Say the name of each picture. Write the letter next to each picture whose name begins with the /f/ sound.

 R 1.14 Match sounds to letters.

fit pot Tom

fit

 fit

pot

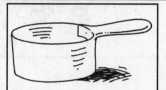

Tom

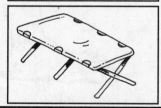

Phonics: Blending *f, o*
Blend the sounds and say the word. Write the word. Then circle the
picture that goes with the word.

 R 1.15 Read one-syllable words.

©Macmillan/McGraw-Hill

Name _____

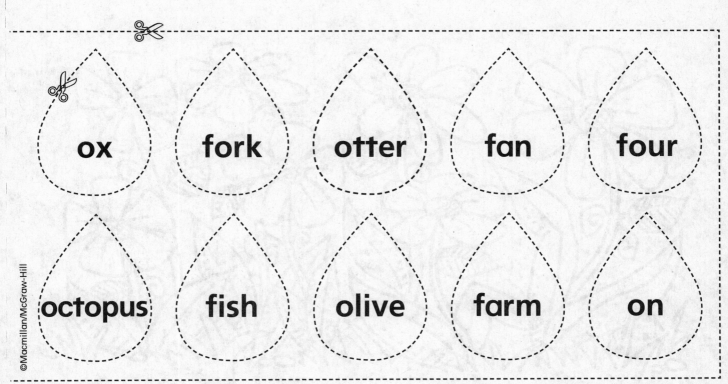

ox	fork	otter	fan	four
octopus	fish	olive	farm	on

Phonics: /o/o, /f/f
Cut out the petals. Look at each word and name its beginning letter and sound. Glue each word on the flower with the same letter as its beginning sound.

CA R 1.14 Match sounds to letters.

©Macmillan/McGraw-Hill

Name _____

_____ _____ _____ _____

o

f

©Macmillan/McGraw-Hill

Phonics: /o/o /f/f
Practice saying and writing the letters o and f.

CA R 1.14 Match sounds to letters.

120 Unit 5: Animals • Week 3

Hh

Name _____

1.

h

2.

3.

Phonics: /h/h
Say the name of each picture. Write the letter below each picture whose name begins with the /h/ sound.

CA R 1.14 Match sounds to letters.

Unit 6: Neighborhood • Week 1   **121**

Name _____

1.

2.

Comprehension: Main Idea and Details
Look at each picture. Tell what you see. What are these pictures
mainly about? I. Circle the picture that shows a boy helping.
2. Circle the picture that shows a girl with her pet.

 R 3.3 Identify events.

©Macmillan/McGraw-Hill

Name _____

We Are

We are at the store.

1

We are home!

@Macmillan/McGraw-Hill

High-Frequency Word: *are*
Read the book aloud to a partner.
Reread for fluency.

CA **R 1.15** Read high-frequency words.

4 Unit 6: Neighborhood • Week 1

We are at the  bakery .

We are at the  park .

Phonemic Awareness: /h/

Look at the picture. Say the name of each item. Circle the item
if its name begins with the same sound you hear at the
beginning of *horse*.

 R 1.11 Distinguish words by
beginning sounds.

 **Write**

Name _____

1.

h**at**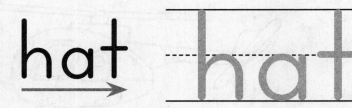

2.

h**am**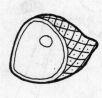

3.

h**ot**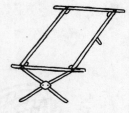

4.

h**op**

Phonics: Blending _h_
Blend the sounds and say the word. Write the word. Circle the
picture that goes with the word.

 **CA** **R 1.15** Read one-syllable words.

©Macmillan/McGraw-Hill

126 Unit 6: Neighborhood • Week I

Dd

Name _____

1.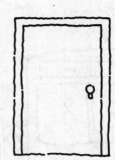

2.

3.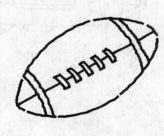

4.

©Macmillan/McGraw-Hill

Phonics: /d/d
Say the name of each picture. Circle the picture whose name begins with the same sound as *duck*. Write the letter.

 R 1.14 Match sounds to letters.

Name _____

1.

2.

Comprehension: Main Idea and Details
Look at each picture. Tell what you see. What are both pictures mainly about? Color the picture that shows an owl going to the eye doctor.

 R 3.3 Identify events.

128 Unit 6: Neighborhood • Week 2

Name _____

For You

I have a cap.

It is for you.

©Macmillan/McGraw-Hill

High-Frequency Words: *for, you*
Read the book aloud to a
partner. Reread for fluency.

 R 1.15 Read high-frequency
words.

4 Unit 6: Neighborhood • Week 2

It is for you.

I have a

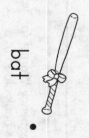
bat

Rr

Name _____

1.

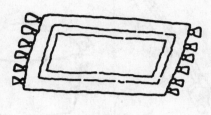   

   r

2.

3.

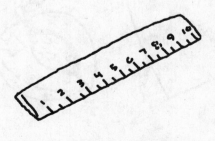   

4.

Phonics: /r/r
Say the name of each picture. Circle the picture whose name begins
with the same sound as *rainbow*. Write the letter.

 R 1.14 Match sounds to letters.

©Macmillan/McGraw-Hill

Name _____

1.

rod →  rod

2.

red →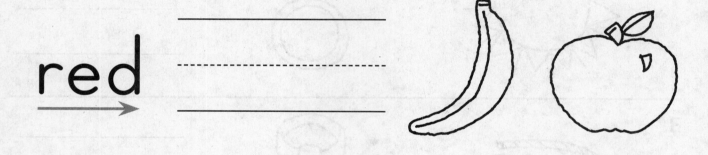

3.

rip →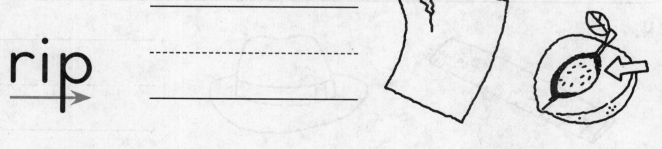

Phonics: Blending r
Blend the sounds and say the word. Write the word. Circle the
picture that goes with the word.

CA R 1.15 Read one-syllable words.

 **Hh**

Name _____

I.       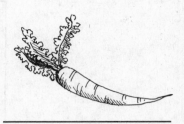

_____   _____   _____

h - - - - - - -   - - - - - - -   - - - - - - -

_____   _____   _____

2.    

_____   _____   _____

- - - - - - -   - - - - - - -   - - - - - - -

_____   _____   _____

3.    

_____   _____   _____

- - - - - - -   - - - - - - -   - - - - - - -

_____   _____   _____

Phonics: /h/h
Say the name of each picture. Write the letter below each picture
whose name begins with the /h/ sound.

 R 1.14 Match sounds to letters.

Unit 6: Neighborhood • Week 3   **133**

Comprehension: Retell
Look at the pictures and listen to the story. *The girl draws a picture. It is for her dad. The girl gives the picture to her dad.* Circle the picture that shows the end of the story. Retell the story to a partner.

CA **R 2.4** Retell familiar stories.

Are You Sad?

Are you sad?

©Macmillan/McGraw-Hill

Name _____

I like you!

High-Frequency Words: are, for, you
Read the book aloud to a partner.
Reread for fluency.

(CA) **R 1.15** Read high-frequency words.

4 Unit 6: Neighborhood • Week 3

I am sad.

I have a
flower
for you.

Dd Rr

1.

d

2.

3.

Phonics: /d/d, /r/r
Say the name of each picture. Then write the letter that stands
for the sound you hear at the beginning of the word. Repeat the
names aloud.

 R 1.14 Match sounds to letters.

Unit 6: Neighborhood • Week 3   137

©Macmillan/McGraw-Hill

1.

I ___**am**___ a cat.

2.

I like to _____.

3.

I _____ nap.

Phonics: Blending am, ap, an
Read the sentence. Write the word that completes the sentence.
Read the sentence again.

(CA) R 1.15 Read one-syllable words.

©Macmillan/McGraw-Hill

Name _____

Phonics: /h/h, /d/d, /r/r, /f/f, /o/o, /k/c
Cut on the dotted lines. Fold on the solid lines and tape together
to make a cube. Toss the cube with a partner. Say the name of the
picture that faces up and its beginning sound and letter. Then say
another word that begins with the same sound and letter.

CA R 1.14 Match sounds to letters.

©Macmillan/McGraw-Hill

Unit 6: Neighborhood • Week 3   **139**

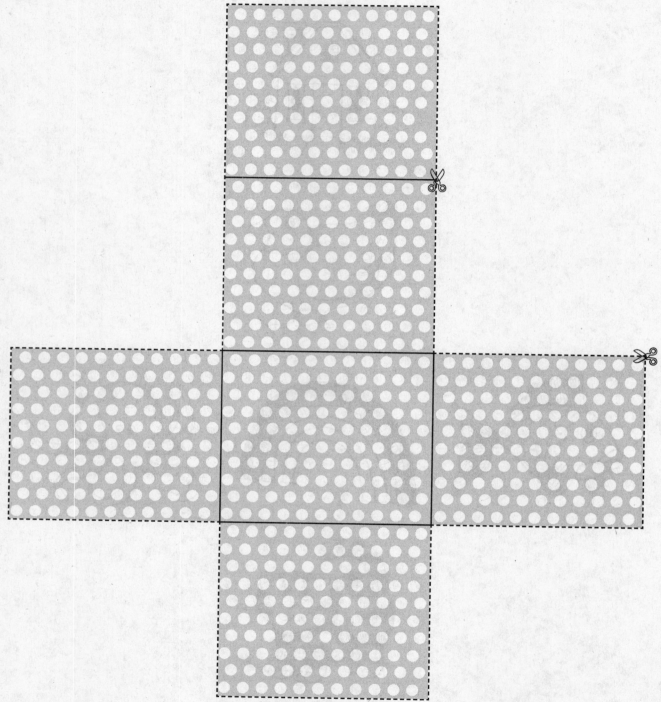

Phonics: /h/h, /d/d, /r/r, /f/f, /o/o, /k/c
Cut on the dotted lines. Fold on the solid lines and tape together
to make a cube.

Ee

Name _____

I.

 _____

 e _____

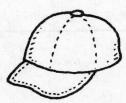 _____

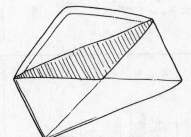 _____

2.

3.

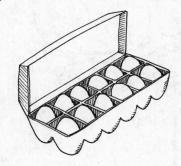 _____

 _____

©Macmillan/McGraw-Hill

Phonics: /e/e
Say the name of each picture. Write the letter next to each
picture whose name begins with the /e/ sound.

CA **R 1.14** Match sounds to letters.

Name _____

I.

2.

Comprehension: Main Idea/Details *A Rainy Day*
Look at each picture. Tell what you see. What are the pictures
mainly about? Circle the pictures that show rainy weather.

 R 3.3 Identify events.

Name _____

I can do this!

High-Frequency Words: *this, do*
Read the book aloud to a partner.
Reread for fluency.

4 Unit 7: Weather • Week 1

Can You?

©Macmillan/McGraw-Hill

Can you do this?

1

I can do this!

Can you do this?

Name _____

I.

 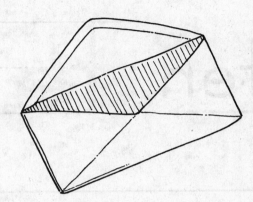

2.

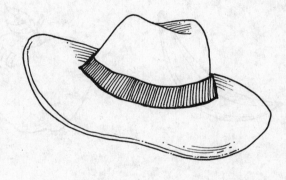 

3.

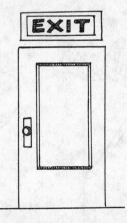 

©Macmillan/McGraw-Hill

Phonemic Awareness: /e/
Say the name of each item. Circle the item if its name begins
with the same sound you hear at the beginning of *egg*.

 R 1.11 Distinguish words by
beginning sounds.

Unit 7: Weather • Week I   **145**

 **Name** _____

I.

ten → ten  10 5

2.

red → _____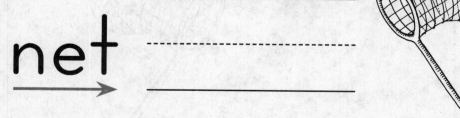

3.

net → _____

Phonics: Blending e
Blend the sounds and say the word. Write the word.
Then circle the picture that goes with the word.

CA **R 1.15** Read one-syllable words.

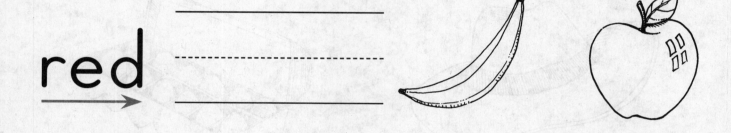

©Macmillan/McGraw-Hill

Bb

Name _____

1.

 _____ **b** _____  _____

2.

_____ _____

3.

 _____ 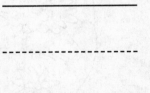 _____

©Macmillan/McGraw-Hill

Phonics: /b/b
Say the name of each picture. Write the letter next to each
picture whose name begins with the /b/ sound.

 R 1.14 Match sounds to letters.

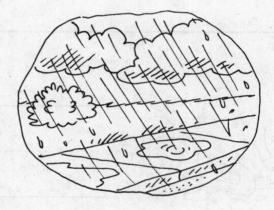

Literary Analysis: Setting
Draw a line from each child to the correct setting.

CA R 3.3 Identify settings.

What Can You Do?

What can you do?

©Macmillan/McGraw-Hill

Name _____

I can sit and nap.

High-Frequency Words: *and, what*
Read the book aloud to a partner.
Reread for fluency.

(CA) R 1.15 Read high-frequency words.

4 Unit 7: Weather • Week 2

I can hop and hop.

What can you do?

LI

Name _____

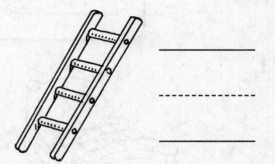

1.

‾ ‾ ‾ ‾ ‾ ‾ ‾ ‾ ‾ ‾ ‾
- - - - - - - - - - -
_____

‾ ‾ ‾ ‾ ‾ ‾ ‾ ‾ ‾ ‾ ‾
- - - - - - - - - - -
_____

2.

‾ ‾ ‾ ‾ ‾ ‾ ‾ ‾ ‾ ‾ ‾
- - - - - - - - - - -
_____

‾ ‾ ‾ ‾ ‾ ‾ ‾ ‾ ‾ ‾ ‾
- - - - - - - - - - -
_____

3.

‾ ‾ ‾ ‾ ‾ ‾ ‾ ‾ ‾ ‾ ‾
- - - - - - - - - - -
_____

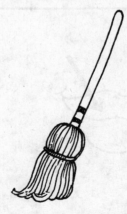

‾ ‾ ‾ ‾ ‾ ‾ ‾ ‾ ‾ ‾ ‾
- - - - - - - - - - -
_____

Phonics: /l/
Say the name of each picture. Write the letter next to each
picture whose name begins with the /l/ sound.

 R 1.14 Match sounds to letters.

Name _____

bed bib lip

1.

(bed)
bit

bed

2.

pen
bib

_____

3.

lip
lap

_____

Phonics: Blending _b, l_
Blend the sounds and say each word. Look at the picture.
Circle the word that goes with the picture. Write the word.

 R 1.15 Read one-syllable words.

©Macmillan/McGraw-Hill

Ee

Name _____

I.

_ _ _ _ _ _ _
e

_ _ _ _ _ _ _

2.

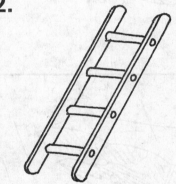

_ _ _ _ _ _ _

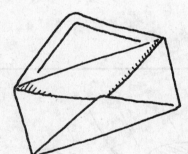

_ _ _ _ _ _ _

3.

EXIT

_ _ _ _ _ _ _

_ _ _ _ _ _ _

©Macmillan/McGraw-Hill

Phonics: /e/e
Say the name of each picture. Write the letter next to each picture
whose name begins with the /e/ sound.

R 1.14 Match sounds to letters.

Name _____

1.

 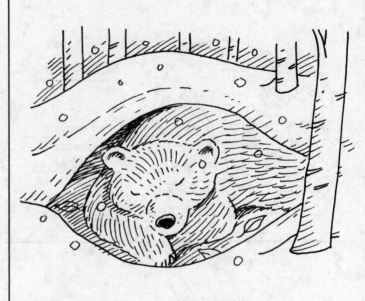

2.

Literary Analysis: Fantasy/Reality
Look at each picture. Circle the picture that shows something
that might really happen. Draw a line under the picture that
shows something that could not happen.

 R 3.1 Distinguish fantasy
from realistic text.

154 Unit 7: Weather • Week 3

©Macmillan/McGraw-Hill

We Can Do This

What can you and I do?

1

Name _____

We can do this.

High-Frequency Words: *this, do, and, what* Read the book aloud to a partner. Reread for fluency.

 R 1.15 Read high-frequency words.

4 Unit 7: Weather • Week 3

We can do this.

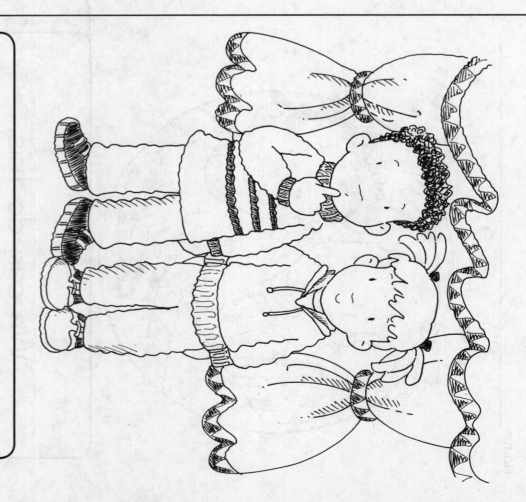

What can you and I do?

Bb Ll

Name _____

1.

b   l

2.

3.

Phonics: /b/b, /l/l
Say the name of each picture. Write the letter *b* below the picture
if its name begins with the same sound as *bear*. Write the letter *l* if
its name begins with the same sound as *leaf*.

 R 1.14 Match sounds to letters.

Unit 7: Weather • Week 3   **157**

sip pit lid

1.

sip

2.

3.

Phonics: Blending *ip, it, id*
Blend the sounds and say each word. Look at the picture.
Write the word that goes with the picture.

  R 1.15 Read one-syllable words.

Name _____

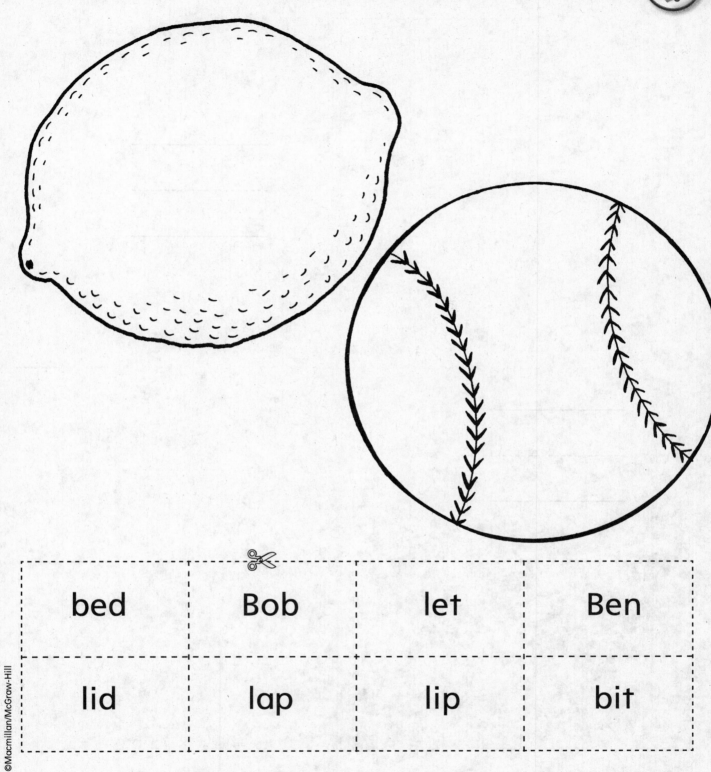

bed	Bob	let	Ben
lid	lap	lip	bit

©Macmillan/McGraw-Hill

Phonics: /e/e, /b/b, /l/l
Cut out each word. Blend the sounds and say each word. Glue each word that begins with the /b/ sound on the *baseball*. Glue each word that begins with the /l/ sound on the lemon.

CA R 1.14 Match sounds to letters.

Name _____

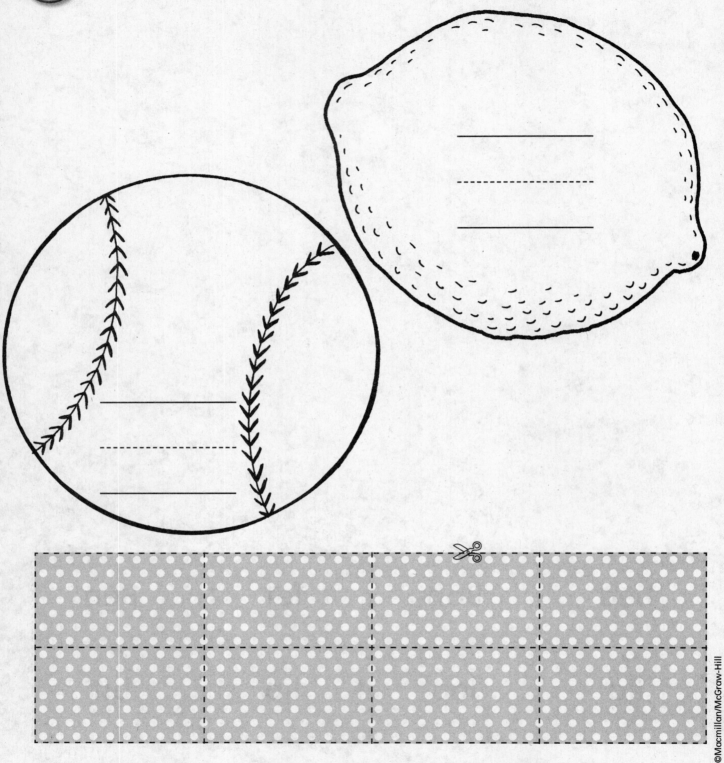

Phonics: /e/e, /b/b, /l/l

Say the name of each item. Write the letter that stands for the /b/ sound you hear at the beginning of the word *baseball*. Write the letter that stands for the /l/ sound you hear at the beginning of the word *lemon*.

160 Unit 7: Weather • Week 3

Kk

Name _____

Write

I.

k _____

2.

3.

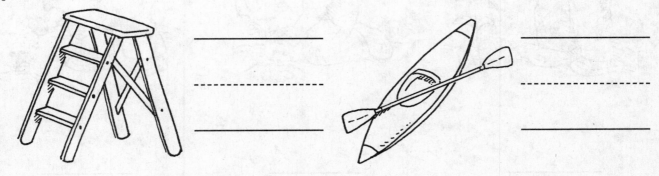

Phonics: /k/k
Say the name of each picture. Write the letter next to each
picture whose name begins with the /k/ sound.

 R 1.14 Match sounds to letters.

©Macmillan/McGraw-Hill

Unit 8: Plants • Week 1 **161**

I.

_____   _____   _____

2.

_____   _____   _____

Comprehension: Sequence
Look at the pictures in each row. Write I, 2, and 3 to show what
happened first, next, and last.

 R 2.3 Connect events to life
experiences.

©Macmillan/McGraw-Hill

It Is Little

This is a flower

Name _____

"It is little," said Pat.

@Macmillan/McGraw-Hill

High-Frequency Words: *little, said*
Read the book aloud to a partner.
Reread for fluency.

CA **R 1.15** Read high-frequency words.

4 Unit 8: Plants • Week 1

①

"It is little," said Ken.

This is a 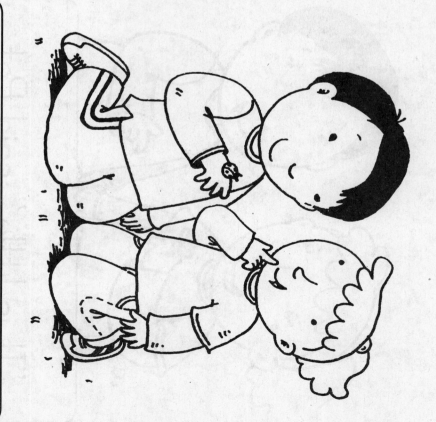 bug .

Name _____

I.

2.

3.

©Macmillan/McGraw-Hill

Phonemic Awareness: /k/
Say the name of each picture. Circle the picture if its name
begins with the same sound you hear at the beginning of *kite*.

 R 1.11 Distinguish words by
beginning sounds.

Name _____

I.

_____
- - - - - - - c k - - - - - - -
_____

2.

_____
- - - - - - - - - - - - - - - - - -
_____

3.

_____
- - - - - - - - - - - - - - - - - -
_____

4.

_____
- - - - - - - - - - - - - - - - - -
_____

Phonics: /k/ck
Say the name of each picture. Write the letters that stand for the
/k/ sound you hear at the end of the word. Repeat the names aloud.

 R 1.14 Match sounds to letters.

©Macmillan/McGraw-Hill

U u

Name _____

Write

I.

_____

_ _ _ _ _ _ _ _ _ _

u

_____

_ _ _ _ _ _ _ _ _ _

2.

_____

_ _ _ _ _ _ _ _ _ _

_____

_ _ _ _ _ _ _ _ _ _

3.

 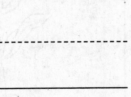

_____

_ _ _ _ _ _ _ _ _ _

_____

_ _ _ _ _ _ _ _ _ _

Phonics: /u/ u
Say the name of each picture. Write the letter next to each picture
whose name begins with the /u/ sound.

CA **R 1.14** Match sounds to letters.

Name _____

I.

2.

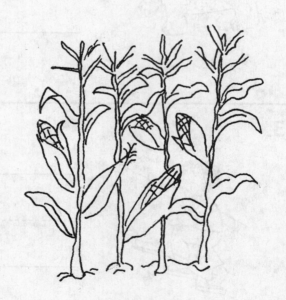

Comprehension: Retell *Seed Secrets*
Use the pictures to retell what happened in the story to a partner.
Color the pictures.

CA **R 2.4** Retell familiar stories.

©Macmillan/McGraw-Hill

We Are Here!

Tim Kim Dan

Tim

Tim was here.

Name _____

We are here!

©Macmillan/McGraw-Hill

High-Frequency Words: *here, was*
Read the book aloud to a partner.
Reread for fluency.

(CA) **R 1.15** Read high-frequency words.

(4) Unit 8: Plants • Week 2

2

Kim was here.

Dan was here.

3

Name _____

©Macmillan/McGraw-Hill

Phonemic Awareness: /u/
Look at the pictures. Say the name of each item. Circle the
item if its name begins with the same sound you hear at the
beginning of *umbrella*.

CA **R 1.11** Distinguish words by beginning sounds.

Unit 8: Plants • Week 2   **171**

Name _____

sun cup pup

1.

sun → _____ sun _____

2.

cup → _____

3.

pup → _____

Phonics: Blending _u_
Blend the sounds and say the word. Write the word. Then circle the picture that goes with the word.

 R 1.15 Read one-syllable words.

©Macmillan/McGraw-Hill

Kk

Name _____

I.

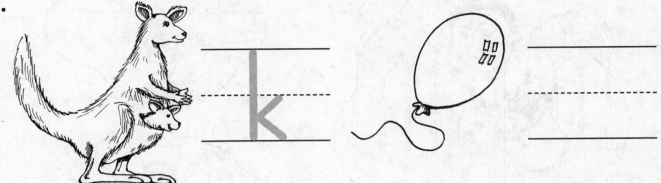

k _____

2.

3.

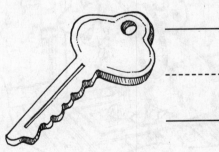

©Macmillan/McGraw-Hill

Phonics: /k/k
Say the name of each picture. Write the letter next to each
picture whose name begins with the /k/ sound.

 CA R 1.14 Match sounds to letters.

Unit 8: Plants • Week 3   173

Draw

Name _____

I.

2.

©Macmillan/McGraw-Hill

Comprehension: Draw Conclusions
Look at the picture on the left. Draw a line to the picture on the
right that shows what may happen.

 R 2.3 Connect events to life experiences.

This Is Little

"This is little," said Nat.

①

Name _____

Bud was a little cub.

High-Frequency Words: *little, said, here, was*
Read the book aloud to a partner.
Reread for fluency.

CA **R 1.15** Read high-frequency words.

④ Unit 8: Plants • Week 3

2

"This is little," said Dot.

"Here is Bud!" said Dot.

3

Uu

Name _____

I.

u

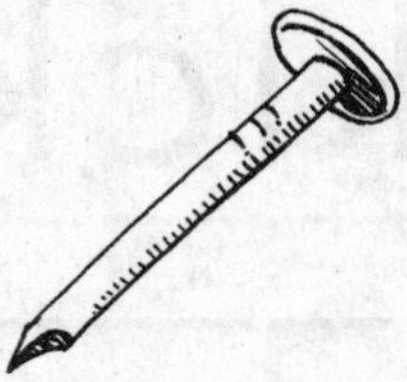

2.

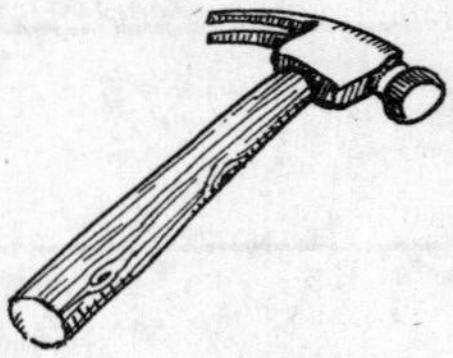

3.

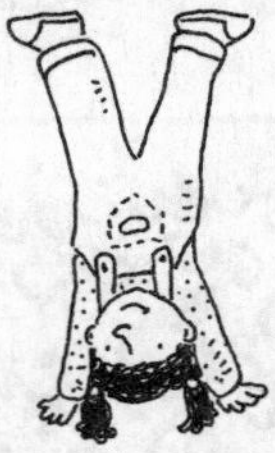

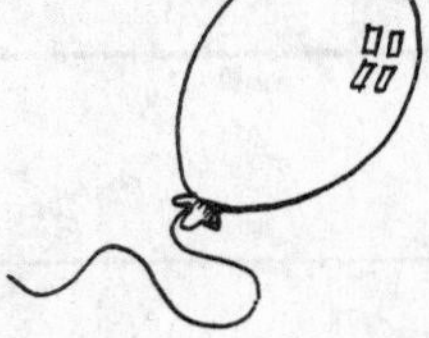

Phonics: /u/u
Say the name of each picture. Write the letter below each
picture whose name begins with the /u/ sound.

 R 1.14 Match sounds to letters.

Name _____

sick kick pick

1.

sick   <u>sick</u>

2.

kick   _____

3.

pick   _____

Phonics: Blending *ick*
Blend the sounds and say the word. Write the word.

 R 1.15 Read one-syllable words.

Name _____

i

u

sun

kick

fun

kit

pup

sick

©Macmillan/McGraw-Hill

Phonics: */i/i, /u/u, /k/k, /k/ck*

Cut out the leaves. Read the words. If a leaf has a word with the /i/ sound, glue it next to the letter *i*. If a leaf has a word with the /u/ sound, glue it next to the letter *u*.

CA R 1.14 Match sounds to letters.

Name _____

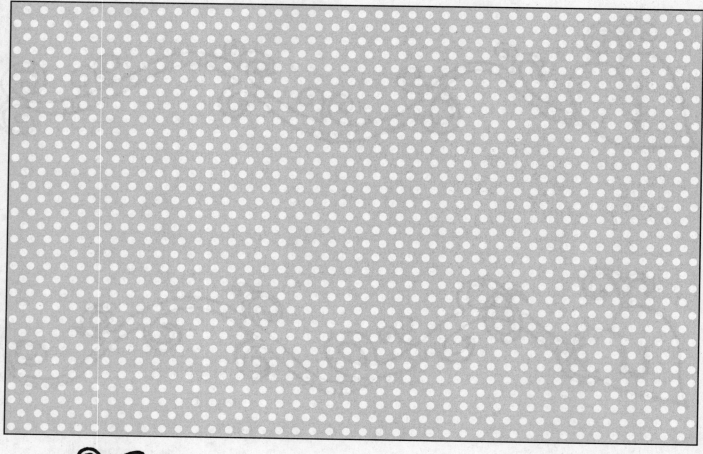

Phonics: /i/i, /u/u, /k/k, /k/ck
Cut out the leaves. Read the words. If a leaf has a word with the /i/ sound, glue it next to the letter *i*. If a leaf has a word with the /u/ sound, glue it next to the letter *u*.

180 Unit 8: Plants • Week 3

©Macmillan/McGraw-Hill

Gg

Name _____

Write

I.  _____
g
_____

 _____
_____

2.  _____
_____

 _____
_____

3.  _____
_____

 _____
_____

4.  _____
_____

 _____
_____

©Macmillan/McGraw-Hill

Phonics: /g/g
Say the name of each picture. Write the letter next to each picture
whose name begins with the /g/ sound.

 R 1.14 Match sounds to letters.

Unit 9: Amazing Creatures • Week I   181

I.

2.

3.

Vocabulary: Classify and Categorize
Look at each picture. Draw an X on the picture that
does not belong. Tell why it does not belong.

 R 1.17 Sort words into categories.

©Macmillan/McGraw-Hill

Kim and Dan

She is Kim.

Name _____

He can hop.

High-Frequency Words: *she, he*
Read the book aloud to a partner.
Reread for fluency.

R 1.15 Read high-frequency words.

4   Unit 9: Amazing Creatures • Week 1

She can run.

He is Dan.

Ww

Name _____

1.

_____

W -------  _____

2.

_____

-------  _____

3.

_____

-------  _____

4.

_____

-------  _____

©Macmillan/McGraw-Hill

Phonics: /w/w
Say the name of each picture. Write the letter next to each
picture whose name begins with the /w/ sound.

 R 1.14 Match sounds to letters.

Name _____

web wet wig

1.

web

_____

web

2.

wet

_____

3.

wig

_____

Phonics: Blending w
Blend the sounds and say the word. Write the word. Circle the
picture that goes with the word.

 R 1.15 Read one-syllable words.

©Macmillan/McGraw-Hill

Name _____

1.

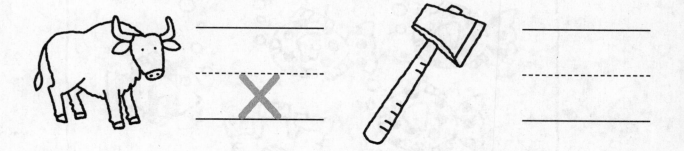

x

2.

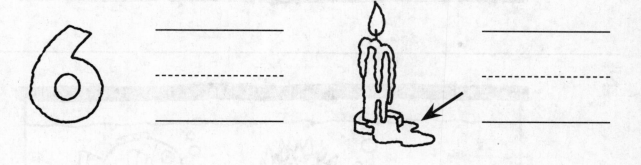

3.

Rex

Phonics: /ks/x
Say the name of each picture. Write the letter that stands for the
/ks/ sound you hear at the end of each word.

CA R 1.14 Match sounds to letters.

Name _____

I.

2.

Comprehension: Compare and Contrast *Fish Faces*
Look at each picture. Circle all the fish that are the same.
Draw an X on the fish that is different. Tell how the fish
are the same and different.

CA **R 1.18** Describe objects in specific language.

Look At This

Look at this .
ladybug

1

Name _____

It has 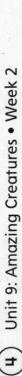.
stripes

High-Frequency Words: *has, look*
Read the book aloud to a partner.
Reread for fluency.

(CA) R 1.15 Read high-frequency words.

4 · Unit 9: Amazing Creatures · Week 2

It has  spots .

Look at this  bee .

Vv

Name _____

I.

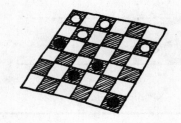

_____

- - - - - - - - - - -

_____

_____

- - - - - - - - - V

_____

2.

_____

- - - - - - - - - - -

_____

_____

- - - - - - - - - - -

_____

3.

_____

- - - - - - - - - - -

_____

_____

- - - - - - - - - - -

_____

4.

_____

- - - - - - - - - - -

_____

_____

- - - - - - - - - - -

_____

©Macmillan/McGraw-Hill

Phonics: /v/v
Say the name of each picture. Write the letter next to
each picture whose name begins with the /v/ sound.

 CA **R 1.14** Match sounds to letters.

Name _____

1.  pig

(six) _____

six

2.  box _____

bag _____

3.  vet _____

web _____

4.  pan _____

van _____

Phonics: Blending x, v
Look at the picture. Blend the sounds and say each word. Circle the word that goes with the picture. Then write the word.

 R 1.15 Read one-syllable words.

Unit 9: Amazing Creatures • Week 2

Name _____

I.

_____

- - - - - - - - - - - - - - -

g

_____

2.

 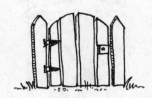 

_____

- - - - - - - - - - - - - - -

_____

3.

_____

- - - - - - - - - - - - - - -

_____

4.

_____

- - - - - - - - - - - - - - -

_____

Phonics: /g/g, /w/w
I. 2. Say the name of each picture. Circle each picture whose
name begins with the same sound as *gate*. Write the letter.
3. 4. Say the name of each picture. Circle each picture whose
name begins with the same sound as *wagon*. Write the letter.

 R 1.14 Match sounds to letters.

Unit 9: Amazing Creatures • Week 3   **193**

Name _____

1.

2.

Literary Analysis: Fantasy and Reality
Look at each picture. Circle the one that shows something that might really happen. Draw a line under the one that shows something that could not happen.

 R 3.1 Distinguish fantasy from realistic text.

Ben and Kat

Look at Ben.

Name

She has a fan.

High-Frequency Words: *she, he, look, has*
Read the book aloud with a partner.
Reread for fluency.

 R 1.15 Read high-frequency words.

He has a top.

Look at Kat!

X x **V v**

Name _____

1. _____
       - - - - - - - - - -
              X

2. _____
       - - - - - - - - - -
       _____

3. _____
       - - - - - - - - - -
       _____

4. _____
       - - - - - - - - - -
       _____

Phonics: /ks/x, /v/v

1. 2. Say the name of each picture. Circle each picture whose name ends with the same sound as *fox*. Write the letter.

3. 4. Say the name of each picture. Circle each picture whose name begins with the same sound as *van*. Write the letter.

CA **R 1.14** Match sounds to letters.

©Macmillan/McGraw-Hill

Unit 9: Amazing Creatures • Week 3   **197**

1.

Ned
Deb

Ned

2.

red
bed

3.

pen
pot

4.

ten
top

Phonics: Blending _ed, en_
Look at each picture. Blend the sounds to read each word. Circle the
word that goes with the picture. Then write the word.

 R 1.15 Read one-syllable words.

©Macmillan/McGraw-Hill

Name _____

Phonemic Awareness: /g/, /w/
Say the name of each picture. Put a marker on each picture whose
name begins with the same sound as *gate*. Play again. Put a marker
on each picture whose name begins with the same sound as *wagon*.

 R 1.11 Distinguish words by
beginning sounds.

Unit 9: Amazing Creatures • Week 3   199

Name _____

Phonemic Awareness: /ks/, /v/
Say the name of each picture. Put a marker on each picture whose
name ends with the same sound as *fox*. Play again. Put a marker on
each picture whose name begins with the same sound as *van*.

R 1.11 Distinguish words by
beginning and ending sounds.

J j

Name _____

Write

1.

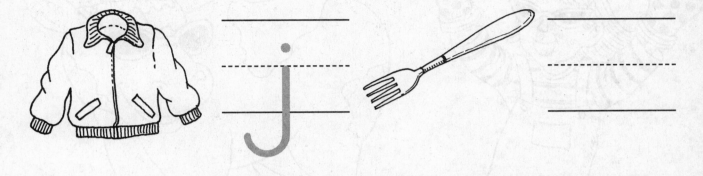

2.

3.

©Macmillan/McGraw-Hill

Phonics: /j/j
Say the name of each picture. Write the letter next to
each picture whose name begins with the /j/ sound.

 R 1.14 Match sounds to letters.

Unit 10: I Know A Lot! • Week 1   **201**

Name _____

©Macmillan/McGraw-Hill

Comprehension: Use Illustrations *What Do You Know!*
Look at the picture. Circle the things that come in twos.

CA R 1.18 Describe objects in general language.

My Dog Mack

This is my dog Mack.

Name _____

I nap with Mack.

High-Frequency Words: *with, my*
Read the book aloud to a partner.
Reread for fluency.

CA R 1.15 Read high-frequency words.

4 Unit 10: I Know A Lot! • Week 1

I play with Mack.

Look at my dog go!

Write

Qq **Name** _____

I.

 _____

qu _____

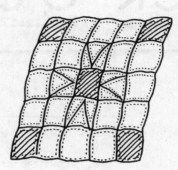 _____

2.

 _____

 _____

3.

 _____

 _____

Phonics: /kw/ qu
Say the name of each picture. Write the letters that stand for
the /kw/ sound you hear at the beginning of each word. Repeat
the names aloud.

 CA R 1.14 Match sounds to letters.

Write

Name _____

quick → Jack → quack →

1.

I am quick.

2.

I like _____.

3.

Jack can _____.

©Macmillan/McGraw-Hill

Phonics: Blending j, qu
Blend the sounds and say the word. Read the sentence.
Write the word that completes the sentence. Read the
sentence again.

CA R 1.15 Read one-syllable words.

Yy

Name _____

I.

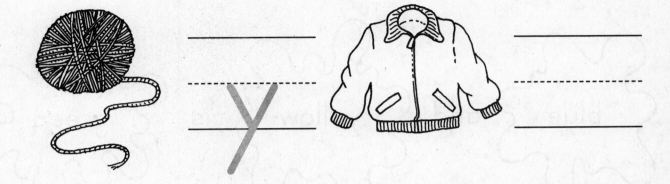

y

2.

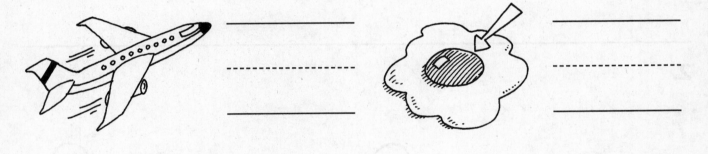

3.

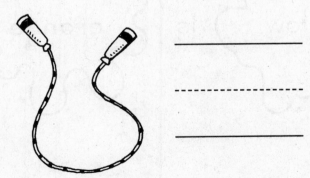

Yogurt

©Macmillan/McGraw-Hill

Phonics: /y/y
Say the name of each picture. Write the letter next to each picture whose name begins with the /y/ sound.

CA **R 1.14** Match sounds to letters.

Name _____

I.

blue and yellow is green

2.

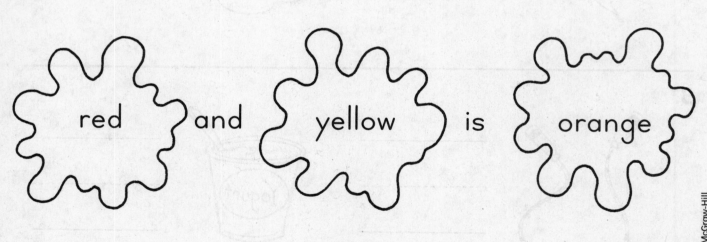

red and yellow is orange

Comprehension: Cause and Effect *Warthogs Paint*
I. Color the first splash blue, the second yellow.
2. Color the first splash red, the second yellow. Mix the 2 colors in the last splash in each row. Name the new colors.

 R 2.3 Connect information to life experiences.

©Macmillan/McGraw-Hill

Name _____

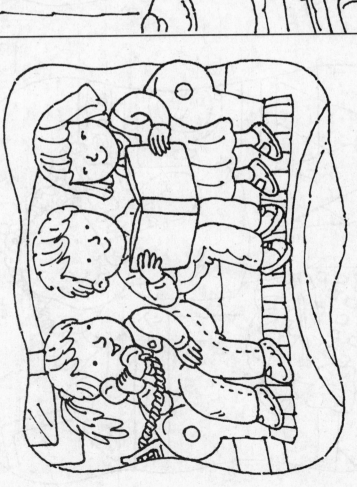

She is here with me.

©Macmillan/McGraw-Hill

High-Frequency Words: *me, where*
Read the book aloud to a partner.
Reread for fluency.

(CA) R 1.15 Read high-frequency words.

(4) Unit 10: I Know A Lot! • Week 2

Where is Jon?

Where is Jon?

(1)

He is here with me.

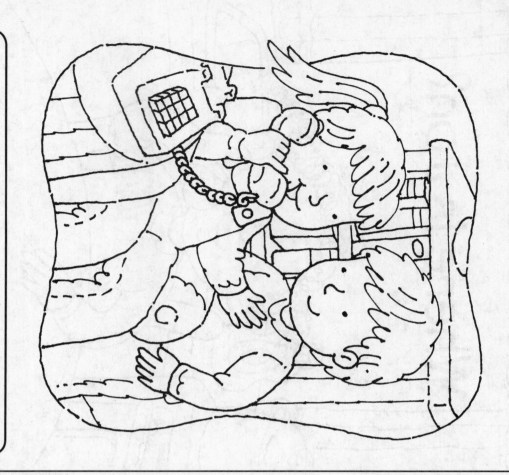

Where is Kat?

Zz

Name _____

Write

I.

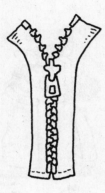

_____

z

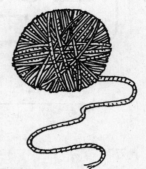

_____

2.

0

_____

_____

3.

_____

_____

Phonics: /z/z
Say the name of each picture. Write the letter next to
each picture whose name begins with the /z/ sound.

CA R 1.14 Match sounds to letters.

Zeb zip

1.

I am __Zeb__.

2.

I can _____.

3.

I like to _____.

Phonics: Blending z
Blend the sounds and say the word. Read each sentence.
Write the word that completes the sentence. Read it again.

 R 1.15 Read one-syllable words.

©Macmillan/McGraw-Hill

| Jj | Qq | **Name** _____ | Write |

1.

qu   j   _____

2.

3.

Phonics: /j/j, /kw/qu
Say the name of each picture. Then write the letter that stands
for the sound you hear at the beginning of the word. Repeat
the names aloud.

CA R 1.14 Match sounds to letters.

I.

2.

Literary Analysis: Setting
I. Look at the pictures. Circle the one that shows animals at a pond.
2. Look at the pictures. Circle the one that shows animals in a tree.

 R 3.3 Identify settings.

©Macmillan/McGraw-Hill

Where Is My Bat?

Where is my bat?

Name _____

It is here with me.

High-Frequency Words: *with, my, me, where*
Read the book aloud to a partner.
Reread for fluency.

CA **R 1.15** Read high-frequency words.

Unit 10: I Know A Lot! • Week 3

It is here with me.

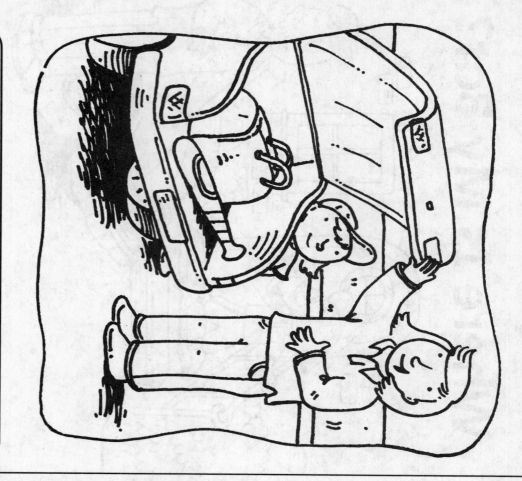

Where is my bag?

Yy   Zz

Name _____

1.

_____   _____   _____

- - - - - - - - y   - - - - - - - - -   - - - - - - - - -

_____   _____   _____

2.

_____   O   _____

- - - - - - - - -   - - - - - - - - -   - - - - - - - - -

_____   _____   _____

3.

_____   _____   _____

- - - - - - - - -   - - - - - - - - -   - - - - - - - - -

_____   _____   _____

©Macmillan/McGraw-Hill

Phonics: /y/y, /z/z
Say the name of each picture. Then write the letter that stands
for the sound you hear at the beginning of the word. Repeat the
names aloud.

 R 1.14 Match sounds to letters.

Unit I0: I Know A Lot! • Week 3   **217**

Name _____

run pup nut

1.

My pup and I <u>run</u>.

2.

My _____ has fun.

3.

He has a _____.

Phonics: Blending _un, up, ut_
Blend the sounds and say the word. Read the sentence. Write the
word that completes the sentence. Read the sentence again.

CA **R 1.15** Read one-syllable words.

jet

cot

sun   fan   pig

sick

Phonics: *Rhyming Words*
Cut on the dotted lines. Fold on the solid lines and tape together.
Take turns tossing the cube with a partner. Read the word that
ends up on top. Then say a word that rhymes with it.

 R 1.10 Produce rhyming words.

Name _____

Phonics: *Rhyming Words*
Cut on the dotted lines. Fold on the solid lines and tape together.
Use to play a game with a partner.